Introductory
Electricity
SECOND EDITION

Introductory
Electricity
SECOND EDITION

Frank J. Long, B.Sc., M.I.E.E.E.
Technological Studies Consultant
Niagara South Board of Education
Curriculum Resources Centre
Allanburg, Ontario

Technical Consultant
John W. Sturrock
Ancaster High and Vocational School
Ancaster, Ontario

General Publishing Co. Limited
Don Mills, Ontario

First Edition published 1965.
First Revised Edition published 1969.
Second Edition published 1976 by
General Publishing Co. Limited
30 Lesmill Road
Don Mills, Ont. M3B 2T6

Designed by Brant Cowie/Artplus
Illustrated by David C. Lunn and Julian Cleva
Photographs by Charles Wright

ISBN 0-7736-5012-1

Fourth Printing, Second Edition 1981

Canadian Cataloguing in Publication Data

Long, Frank J., 1924—
Introductory electricity

For grade 9 in Ontario.
Includes index.
ISBN 0-7736-5012-1

1. Electricity.   I. Sturrock, John W.
II. Title.

QC523.L65 1976   537   C76-017129-7

Introductory Electricity, Second Edition has been prepared for use as a classroom text, rather than as a reference book. All text materials and illustrations have been up-dated, and information on metrication has been included. As well, most sections have been expanded and a completely new section (Hand Tools) has been added. Additional experiments and projects have also been included.

The objectives of this *Second Edition* are the same as those of the earlier editions, that is, to present the material in a logical teaching sequence and to meet the curriculum requirements set down for introductory courses in electricity. There is great emphasis both on fundamental principles and their practical applications.

All references made to the Hydro Code are from the fifteenth edition of the Ontario Hydro Regulations.

I wish to thank the following for their invaluable assistance in the preparation of this text: my wife Joyce for her research and typing; Charles Wright, photographer; Ewart Davies, for his valuable editorial advice during preparation of the original text; Henry Froese, Co-ordinator of the Work Experience Program, Lincoln County (Ontario) Board of Education, for his thorough and painstaking research during the preparation of the illustrative material for the original text. Thanks also to Bill McPherson of Sir John A. Macdonald Collegiate, Scarborough, Ontario, for his assistance with the preparation of the cover design.

Frank J. Long

Preface

Contents

Introductory
Electricity
SECOND EDITION

1 The Electrical Age

This is the electrical age. Electricity is a reasonably economical and easily transportable form of power. It can be used in small amounts to operate appliances such as razors, radios, clocks, telephones and television sets. In large amounts it can be used to light and heat our homes, and to operate motors in factories, trains, and street cars.

Developments in the field of electricity during the last 30 or 40 years read like a fairy tale. If electricity were suddenly turned off or became unavailable the adverse results would be almost impossible to calculate. Could you imagine the terrible backward step it would be if we were forced to do away with the electric light, let alone the radio and telephone?

Electricity has made great contributions to putting man on the moon and in the conquering of outer space. Yet, even with all the progress made in electricity, scientists tell us that it is still in its infancy; its future is almost beyond foretelling or guessing.

Yes, indeed, this is the electrical age.

Theory of Electricity

What is electricity? Scientists have been searching over two hundred years for an answer to that question. Each time they discover a new fact, they realize there is still much more to learn.

The Greeks, about 2000 years ago, discovered that some light dry materials were attracted to amber (a hard yellowish substance) when it was rubbed with cloth or fur. In 1600, William Gilbert named the attraction *electricity* from the Greek word for amber: *elektron*.

Other scientists since have found that certain objects either attract or repel each other. These objects are said to be electrified or charged. One charge

The Electron Theory

is called *positive* and the other *negative.*
Further investigation found that:
*Like charges repel and unlike charges
attract* (See Figure 1.1)

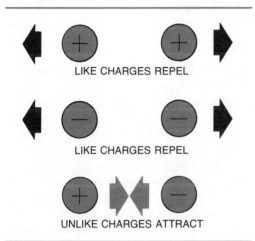

LIKE CHARGES REPEL

LIKE CHARGES REPEL

UNLIKE CHARGES ATTRACT

Figure 1.1   Law of charges

Electron Theory

The modern theory concerning electricity is the *Electron Theory.* Investigation has suggested that the flow of electricity along a conductor is simply a stream of minute particles called *electrons.* The movement of these electrons is caused by electrical pressure. This is similar to water pressure causing water to flow in a pipe. The movement of electrons is called electricity in motion or *electrical current.*

In earlier years, it was assumed that electricity flowed from positive to negative. This flow is known as the *conventional method of current flow.* Benjamin Franklin's experimental work and ideas contributed to this theory and it is still widely used. However, the discovery of the electron by Joseph Thompson in 1897 (Thompson's *Electron Flow Theory*) proves that electrons flow from *negative to positive.*

In our studies in electricity and electric circuits we will assume the Electron Theory, that is, from *negative to positive.*

Kinds of Electricity

There are two kinds of electricity: (1) *static* and (2) *dynamic* or *current.* Static electricity is electricity at rest. Dynamic or current electricity is electricity in motion.

Dynamic or current electricity may also be classified as *alternating current,* ac, or *direct current,* dc. Alternating current is obtained from generators and is the type of electricity used in houses for lighting and power. Direct current is obtained from batteries and dry cells and is used in flashlights and portable radios.

For Review

1. How did electricity get its name?
2. What is amber?
3. What are the two charges when a substance is electrified?
4. State the Law of Charges.
5. Explain static electricity.
6. What causes electrons to move?
7. Explain electric current.
8. According to the Electron Theory, in what direction does electricity flow?
9. What is the assumed or conventional method of current flow?
10. Name two kinds of electricity and explain how they are classified.
11. What type of electricity is obtained from a dry cell?
12. What type of electricity is used in your home?

Methods to Produce Electron Flow

Electrons can be made to flow by applying certain types of pressures. The six types of pressures that cause this flow are: (1) friction, (2) chemical action, (3) magnetism, (4) mechanical, (5) heat, (6) light.

Electric Charges from Friction.

Figure 1.2 shows the effect of rubbing a glass rod with a piece of silk. As the rod is rubbed it *loses* electrons to the silk and assumes a positive charge.

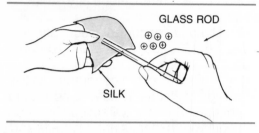

Figure 1.2   Producing a positive charge

Figure 1.3 shows the effect of rubbing a rubber rod with a piece of fur. As the rod is rubbed it *gains* electrons from the fur and assumes a negative charge.

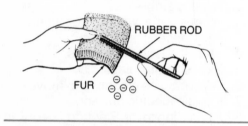

Figure 1.3   Producing a negative charge

The accompanying list of substances, called the *electric series,* is arranged so that each substance is positive to all that follow it in the list and negative to all that precede it; that is, any substance receives a positive charge when rubbed with a substance listed after it in the series. For example, glass when rubbed with silk receives a positive charge and when rubbed with fur receives a negative charge.

THE ELECTRIC SERIES

1. Fur
2. Flannel
3. Ivory
4. Crystals
5. Glass
6. Cotton
7. Silk
8. Leather
9. The Body
10. Wood
11. Metals
12. Sealing Wax
13. Resins
14. Gutta Percha
15. Guncotton

Electric Charges from Chemical Action.

A primary cell consists of two different metals separated from each other and immersed in a solution of sulphuric acid (H_2SO_4) and water (H_2O). This solution is called the *electrolyte.*

Chemical action causes the electrons to leave the solution and enter the zinc. This is the principle of operation of wet cells and batteries.

Dry cells operate on the same principle as wet cells, except that a solid electrolyte is used instead of a liquid. Figure 1.4 shows the construction of a simple cell.

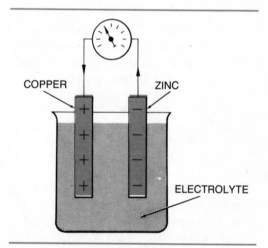

Figure 1.4   Simple cell

Electric Charges from Magnetism.

This is the most common method of producing electricity for electric power. The principle involved is the moving of a wire conductor past a magnet. (See Figure 1.5) The magnetic field induces electron flow in the wire as it passes through the field.

Introductory Electricity

A greater electron flow can be produced either by increasing the speed at which the wire passes through the magnetic field or by increasing the amount of wire cutting through the field. We can increase the amount of wire by using a wire coil with many turns. Moving the magnetic field past a wire or coil will produce the same effect as moving the conductor through the field.

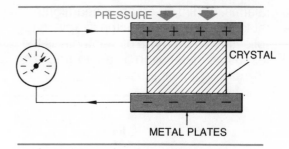

Figure 1.6   Electric charge from pressure

Electric Charges from Heat (Thermal).
If two dissimilar metals, such as copper and iron, are welded together to form a junction and the junction is heated, an electron flow will result. Figure 1.7 shows a simple circuit in which the electric charge is produced from heat.

A junction of this type is called a *thermocouple.* Thermocouples are normally used to operate the meter in heat-indicating devices.

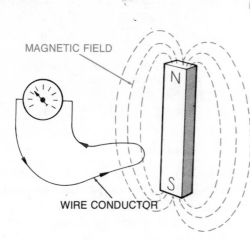

Figure 1.5   Wire cutting through a magnetic field

Electric Charges from Pressure (Piezoelectric).   Crystals of certain materials will produce electron flow if a pressure is exerted on them. Quartz and Rochelle salts are two of these materials. Pressure causes the electrons from the crystal to move in one direction charging one plate negatively and leaving the other plate positively charged. A wire connected across the two plates results in electron flow. The larger the change in pressure the greater the electron flow. This type of electricity is used in record players, dictaphones, and some types of microphones. Figure 1.6 illustrates the principle of operation for a simple piezoelectric cell.

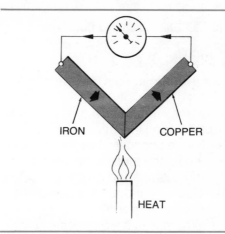

Figure 1.7   Electric charge from heat

Electric Charges from Light (Photo-voltaic).   When light strikes certain materials, such as selenium, electrons can be made to flow. (See Figure 1.8)

This type of electricity is used in industry to perform many automatic functions. Its most common application is in a photoelectric tube or cell (electric eye) used to open doors, count articles on conveyor belts, touch off burglar alarms, or dim automobile headlights automatically. Perhaps the simplest application for this type of electricity is the exposure meter used by photographers to indicate light intensity.

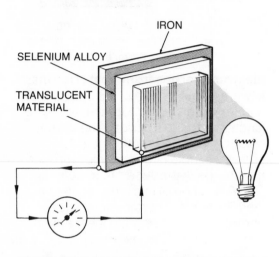

IRON

SELENIUM ALLOY

TRANSLUCENT MATERIAL

Figure 1.8   Electric charge from light

For Review

1. Name four materials that easily build up static electricity.
2. What does the charge of a material depend upon in static electricity?
3. (a) Name two materials that will develop an electric charge if a force is exerted on them.
    (b) Upon what does the size of the charge depend?
    (c) Where is this type of electricity used extensively?
4. (a) Draw a diagram showing how an electric charge can be developed by heat.
    (b) What is this type of junction called?
    (c) Where is this type of electric charge used?
5. (a) Upon what principle does the photo cell operate?
    (b) Describe a practical application for photoelectricity.

pg.13 (handwritten)

pg13 (handwritten)

(c) What are the three basic materials used to produce this type of charge?
6. Name two places where the electric eye may be used.
7. (a) Draw a diagram showing how to produce electricity by chemical action.
    (b) What is the composition of the electrolyte?
    (c) What is this type of cell called?
8. (a) What is the principle of electric charges from magnetism?
    (b) Where is this type of electricity used?
    (c) Does it make any difference which parts move?
    (d) How can the electricity be increased in this method?

Conductors

Materials that allow an electric current to pass through them easily are called *conductors*. Conductors are usually divided into three classes: good, medium, and poor. There is no perfect conductor of electricity.

Listed below, in descending order of conductivity, are a few of the more common materials that are used as conductors.

GOOD CONDUCTORS	
1. Silver	7. Platinum
2. Copper	8. Iron
3. Gold	9. Nickel
4. Aluminum	10. Tin
5. Zinc	11. Lead
6. Brass	12. Mercury

MEDIUM CONDUCTORS	
1. Coke and Charcoal	4. Alkali Solutions
2. Carbon	5. Salt Solutions
3. Acid Solutions	6. Moist Earth

POOR CONDUCTORS	
1. Linen and Cotton	3. Marble
2. Dry Woods	4. Pure Water

Figure 1.9 Typical insulated wire.

FLAMESEAL 2 TYPE TW 600V

Figure 1.10   Typical insulated cable.

Conductors also may be used as *resistors.* In such an application, the resistor is really a poor conductor of electricity that offers a great opposition to the flow of current.

Uses of Common Conductors

COPPER: electric wires, bus bars, mechanisms, contacts (Figures 1.9 and 1.10)

ALUMINUM: transmission lines, mechanisms, castings on motors, electrical fittings

ZINC: dry cells, batteries, fuse links

BRASS: terminals, screws, plugs, switches, sockets

NICKEL: contact points on switches, relays, parts of electron tubes

LEAD: storage battery plates

MERCURY: silent switches, thermostats, rectifiers

CARBON: dry cells, contacts, brushes

NICHROME: heating elements, rheostats

ELECTROLYTE: batteries, electroplating

TUNGSTEN: filaments for lamps, electron tubes

Insulators and Non-Conductors

Materials that do *not* allow an appreciable amount of electric current to pass through them are called *non-conductors* or *insulators.* Insulators are used to prevent electricity from flowing where it is not desired. There is no such thing as a perfect insulator. With increases in voltage any material known to man will eventually allow electricity to pass through it. A non-conductor may be distinguished by the manner in which it is used. For example, although sealing wax is a non-conductor, it would not be used to insulate copper conductors.

NOTE: Moisture often changes an insulator into a poor conductor and a poor conductor into a medium conductor.

INSULATORS

1. Slate	7. Shellac and Varnish
2. Oils and Paints	8. Ebonite
3. Porcelain	9. Mica
4. Paper	10. Paraffin
5. Wood and Silk	11. Glass and Rubber
6. Sealing Wax	12. Dry Air

Uses of Common Insulators

SLATE: panel boards, switch boards
OILS: transformers, cooling agent in
      large electrical devices
PORCELAIN: wire supports, sockets,
      receptacles (Figure 1.11)

Figure 1.11   Porcelain and glass insulators

SILK: wire insulation
SEALING WAX AND PITCH: dry cells
ENAMELS: wire insulation
MICA: toasters, irons, commutators on
      motors
RUBBER: wire, tapes
GLASS: fuse bodies, lamp bulbs, wire
      supports
BAKELITE: switch bodies, plates, radio
      parts
COTTON: wire insulation, tapes
ASBESTOS: wire insulation in heating
      units
PLASTICS: wire insulation, tapes

For Review

1. What is a conductor of electricity?
2. What is an insulator of electricity?
3. Distinguish between an insulator and a non-conductor.
4. What does moisture do to some non-conductors?
5. State the purpose of an insulator.
6. What appliance makes use of mica?
7. What material is used to insulate switch bodies?
8. Name five good conductors of electricity.
9. What is the most common conductor used for wiring in a home?
10. Name five insulators.
11. What type of insulation is used on the electric wiring in your home?
12. List; in order of conductivity, the four conductors which are most widely used commercially.
13. Where is mercury used as a conductor?
14. What common device makes use of tungsten?
15. What appliance makes use of nichrome?

2

Ohm's Law

Water Circuits

You have probably heard the terms volts, amperes, and ohms used quite often when dealing with electricity. These terms will be explained in this section.

To understand the nature of electricity we will compare it to something you can see: the flow of water. Figure 2.1 illustrates a very simple water circuit.

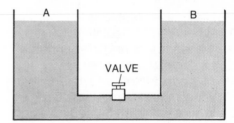

Figure 2.1
No water flow when valve is opened because there is no difference in pressure

No water will flow from tank A to tank B or from B to A because the water level is the same in both tanks. There is no pressure difference, hence, no force motivating flow.

In Figure 2.2, water will flow from A to B because the water in tank A has a higher head pressure (higher water level) than the water in tank B. It can be stated that water will flow if there is a *difference in pressure.*.

In Figure 2.3, pipes a and b have the same length and diameter; however, the water level in tank A is much higher than in tank B. The head pressure in tank A is greater than in tank B and therefore the water flow out of pipe a is greater. In

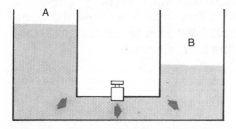
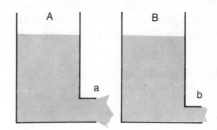

Figure 2.2
Water flows when valve is opened because there is a difference in pressure

other words, there is a difference in motivating pressures. Generally speaking, the greater the pressure the greater the flow through any given orifice.

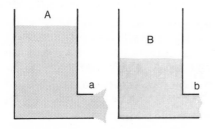

Figure 2.3   Greater rate of flow in pipe *a*

In Figure 2.4, the motivational pressures in tank *A* and tank *B* are the same; however, the flow from pipe *a* is much greater than from pipe *b*. This is because the *diameter* of pipe *a* is greater than the diameter of pipe *b,* thus producing less resistance to flow.

Figure 2.4
Greater rate of flow in pipe *a* because it has less resistance

In Figure 2.5, motivational pressures and pipe diameters are the same for both *a* and *b*; however, the rate of flow from pipe *a* is much greater than from pipe *b*. The rate of flow is less in pipe *b* because it is *longer* and therefore produces greater internal friction. This, in turn, creates greater resistance to flow and reduces the rate of flow.

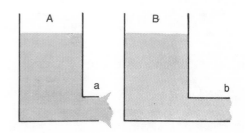

Figure 2.5
Greater rate of flow in pipe *a* because it has less resistance

You have seen that in order for water to flow there must be a *difference in pressure*. Also, a greater rate of flow exists where there is less opposition (*resistance*) to water flow or an increase in pressure. The units of measurement for the water circuit are:

PRESSURE: pascals (Pa)

WATER FLOW: litres per second (L/s)

RESISTANCE: no unit

Electric Circuits

Electric circuits basically follow the same rules regarding pressure and resistance as do water circuits.

In Figure 2.6 note that no electricity (electrons) can flow because there is *no difference in pressure* between the two ends of the wire A and B.

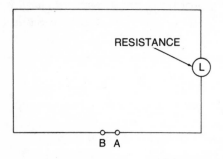

Figure 2.6
No electricity flows because there is no difference in pressure

However, if a dry cell is connected between the two ends of the wire (Figure 2.7) electricity will flow from end A to B. This is because the end of the wire A is now at a higher pressure than B or, in other words, there is a *difference in pressure* between points A and B.

If, in Figure 2.7, the diameter of the wire were made twice as large, it would be reasonable to assume that twice as much electrical current (electrons) would flow. This is because the wire would have less opposition (*resistance*) to the flow of current.

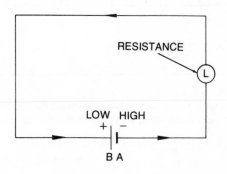

Figure 2.7
Electricity flows because there is a difference in pressure

You now know that in order for electricity to flow there must be a *difference in pressure*. If there is an increase in pressure, there will be an increase in electrical current flow. Also, a greater rate of flow exists where there is less opposition (*resistance*) to the current flow. The units of measurement for the electrical circuit are:

PRESSURE: volts (V)

CURRENT FLOW: amperes (A)

RESISTANCE: ohms (Ω)

The term *volt* is named after a famous Italian scientist, Alessandro Volta. He did extensive work in the development of the voltaic cell which produced an electrical pressure or, as it is termed, *Electromotive Force (E)*.

The term *ampere* is named after the French scientist André Ampère, who actually measured the flow of electricity with a meter. In fact, the first meters to measure current flow were called "ampere meters".

Ohm's Law

The term *ohm* is named after the German scientist Georg Simon Ohm. It was Ohm who discovered the relationship between the pressure, current flow, and resistance in an electrical circuit which today is known as *Ohm's Law*.

This law, stated simply, is that *if a pressure of one volt is exerted on a circuit with a resistance of one ohm, one ampere of current will flow.*

Expressed as a formula, it can be stated as:

$$AMPERES = \frac{PRESSURE}{RESISTANCE} = \frac{VOLTS}{OHMS}$$

Expressed as symbols: $I = E/R$

where I = Current in amperes
E = Pressure in volts
R = Resistance in ohms

This equation may be expressed in two other forms without affecting the relationship:

$$E = I \times R \text{ and } R = E/I$$

Figure 2.8 shows a simple method for remembering Ohm's Law. Consider the horizontal line as a division line and the vertical line as a multiplication line.

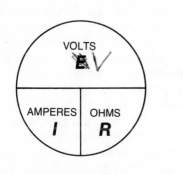

Figure 2.8   **Ohm's Law**

Thus, if you want the formula for I, cover I with your finger, and you will see that it can be found by dividing the volts (E) by the resistance (R). R and E can be found in the same manner.

Example 1
A circuit has a resistance of 10 Ω at a pressure of 120 V. How much current can flow?

Solution: The current (I) equals the voltage (E) divided by the resistance (R) or
$$I = E/R = \frac{120 \text{ V}}{10 \text{ Ω}} = 12A$$

Example 2
A vacuum cleaner motor draws a current of 3 A at a pressure of 120 V. Find the resistance of the motor.

Solution: The resistance (R) equals the voltage (E) divided by the current (I) or
$$R = E/I = \frac{120 \text{ V}}{3 \text{ A}} = 40 \text{ Ω}$$

Example 3
How much pressure is required to force a current of 15 A through a resistance of 8 Ω?

Solution: The pressure (E) equals the current (I) multiplied by the resistance (R) or
$$E = I \times R = 15 \text{ A} \times 8 \text{ Ω} = 120 \text{ V}$$

Ohm's Law is one of the most valuable tools that the electrical worker will use; therefore, it should be learned thoroughly. The use of Ohm's Law for different parts of circuits will be covered later in the course.

For Review

1. Define the following terms and state how each derives its name:
   (a) volt,   (b) ampere,   (c) ohm.
2. What is required in order for electrical current to flow?
3. How can more electrical current be made to flow in a circuit with a fixed resistance?

4. How can less current be made to flow in a circuit with a constant voltage?
5. Write Ohm's Law in words.
6. Express symbolically the three forms of Ohm's Law.
7. Copy the table in your notes and insert the missing values:

AMPERES	OHMS	VOLTS
10	10	—
—	60	120
4	—	100
24	5	—
3.4	—	119
—	50	150
12.5	10.5	—
22	—	220
—	300	60
0.01	100	—

8. What voltage is required to force a current flow of 3 A, if the resistance is 50 Ω ?
9. An electric iron has a resistance of 50 Ω . How much current will flow when the voltage is 120 V?
10. An electric tea kettle operates on 120 V. What resistance does it have if 3.3 A flow?
11. What resistance does a toaster have if the voltage is 120 V and the current flow is 2.5 A?
12. The resistance of an electric lamp is 100 Ω . If the applied voltage is 120 V, how much current flows?

Meters and Measurement of Electricity

Since voltmeters and ammeters are used extensively by the electrician and technician for measuring and testing wiring circuits, transformers, motors, generators, and most electrical apparatus and equipment, it is important that these meters be thoroughly understood.

Voltmeters

The voltmeter is an instrument used to measure electrical pressure or Electromotive Force *(emf)* (voltage). Voltmeters, according to their use, may be either the portable or panel-and-switchboard type. Figure 2.9 shows one type of portable voltmeter.

Figure 2.9   Voltmeter

Voltmeter Connections.   The voltmeter must always be connected in *parallel* across the source whose potential difference (voltage) is to be measured. Figure 2.10 shows how a voltmeter would be connected to measure the voltage across the source terminals.

Care must be taken to connect the *positive terminal* of the voltmeter to the *positive side* of the source terminal, and the *negative terminal* to the *negative* source terminal. If the polarity were reversed, the meter indicating pointer would reverse direction and could possibly be bent or broken. The terminals of the voltmeter are plainly marked positive (+) and negative (−).

Figure 2.10   Measuring the voltage across the source terminals

Ammeters

The ammeter is an instrument used to measure electric current flow or amperes. Ammeters may be either the portable or panel type. Figure 2.11 shows one type of portable ammeter.

Ammeter connections. The ammeter must always be connected in *series* with the load resistance in the circuit whose current flow is to be measured. Figure 2.12 shows how an ammeter would be connected to measure the current flow through a lamp (load resistance).

Care must be taken to connect the *positive terminal* of the ammeter to the *positive terminal* of the source terminal, and the negative terminal to the nega-

Figure 2.11   Ammeter

Ohm's Law

Figure 2.12   Measuring the current flow through a load resistance (lamp)

tive source terminal. Special care must be taken when connecting the ammeter because if it were connected as a voltmeter (across the line) the ammeter would burn out immediately.

How To Read a Meter Scale

Figure 2.13 shows a meter scale with three ranges: 1.5, 15, and 150. When measuring unknown voltages or currents, always connect to the highest range first. This will prevent meter burnouts. If the reading on the meter is too low for accuracy, then connect the meter to the next lower range until an accurate measurement can be read on the scale. To read a meter scale:

Determine what each division equals on each scale, then look directly down on the meter and record.

For example, each division on the 1.5 scale equals 0.02. On the 15 scale,

each division equals 0.2 and on the 150 scale, each division equals 2.

No. 1 readings on the meter are as follows: 0.28 on the 1.5 scale, 2.8 on the 15 scale, and 28 on the 150 scale.

No. 2 readings on the meter are as follows: 1.06 on the 1.5 scale, 10.6 on the 15 scale, and 106 on the 150 scale.

NOTE: When the meter pointer falls between divisions, select the reading nearest the pointer.

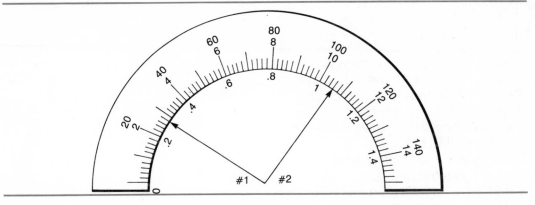

Figure 2.13   A meter scale

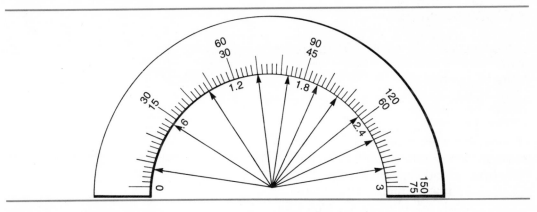

Figure 2.14   A meter scale

For Review

1. State the purpose of (a) a voltmeter, (b) an ammeter.
2. How is a voltmeter connected in a circuit?
3. How is an ammeter connected in a circuit?
4. If an ammeter were connected as a voltmeter, what would happen?
5. If a voltmeter were connected as an ammeter, what would happen?
6. What care must be taken with regard to polarity when connecting a meter?
7. What would happen if the meter were connected with reverse polarity?
8. Make a table as shown in Table 1 in your notes and insert the correct readings for each range of the meter, Figure 2.14, starting from the left.

TABLE 1

Position	3	75	150
1			
2			
3			
4			
5			
6			
7			
8			
9			
10			

Metric Units of Measurement

A new system called the International System of Units, or SI, was adopted in 1960 by the General Conference on Weights and Measures. The principal units of electricity have always been in SI and are listed below:

COULOMB (C) electric charge
VOLT (V) electric pressure
AMPERE (A) electric current
OHM (Ω) electric resistance (omega)
JOULE (J) energy
WATT (W) electric power

Listed below are the *seven base units* of SI:

metre (m) length
kilogram (kg) mass
second (s) time
ampere (A) electric current
candela (cd) light intensity
kelvin (K) temperature
mole (mol) amount of substance

It should be mentioned that Canada has already adopted the Celsius scale for temperature and will be adopting other SI units for mass and measurement.

3

Whenever a current of electricity is flowing through a conductor, the conductor is subject to a *rise in temperature,* because the electrical energy used in forcing the current through the resistance is transformed into heat energy. Conductors that carry small currents and are properly ventilated do not increase too much in temperature. Conductors which carry large currents and are poorly ventilated become very hot.

Fuses

The heating effect of an electric current is used to great advantage in fuses. When current passes through a resistor, *heat is generated* and if the temperature rises too high, the resistor will melt.

Fuses are metal resistors with very low resistance values. They are usually made of an alloy of lead and tin. Fuses are connected in *series* in a circuit, thus, if the fuse "blows", the circuit is opened. Fuses are constructed so they will blow at any predetermined amperage. We have 2 A, 5 A, 15 A, and many other fuses. Never insert fuses which have a higher rating than the current-carrying capacity of the conductor in the circuit because there will be no protection against overloads or short circuits and serious damages may result.

Plug Fuses. The common plug-type fuse is shown in Figure 3.1. The fusible link is enclosed in a sturdy glass housing which prevents the molten metal from splattering when the fuse blows. The largest size approved in the plug type is 30 A. It is the most common type of fuse used for branch lighting circuits in the home and should have a 15 A rating. Once these fuses blow, they are discarded and replaced by another.

Cartridge Fuses. The cartridge type of fuse is used widely in industry and is the only type that can be used when the current is more than 30 A. There are two

Heating Effects of Electric Current

Figure 3.1   Plug fuse—15 A

basic types of cartridge fuses: renewable and non-renewable. A non-renewable fuse with ferrule contact is shown in Figure 3.2. This ferrule construction is used only on fuses rated at 60 A or less.

Figure 3.2
Non-renewable cartridge fuse—30 A

Figure 3.3   Glass cartridge fuse

The 40 A cartridge fuse is used for electric ranges in the home. There are special smaller cartridge fuses that are used in meters, automobiles, and motor circuits.

Knife-Blade Fuses. This fuse, Figure 3.4, is the knife-blade contact type and is used in the home for the main service over-current devices in the main switch box. Knife-blade construction is used only on fuses rated at 61 A or more.

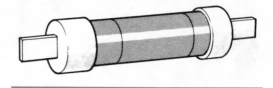

Figure 3.4
Knife-blade cartridge fuse—100 A

Renewable fuses. Cartridge and knife-blade fuses may be non-renewable or renewable. The non-renewable type, once blown, is of no further value. However, the renewable type can have its fusible links replaced. Most industrial plants use the renewable type fuses even though they are initially more costly. A 30 A cartridge renewable link is shown in Figure 3.5.

Figure 3.5   30 A cartridge fuse link

Detailed construction of the renewable link in a knife-blade fuse is shown in Figure 3.6. The 100 A knife-blade fuse is used in the main service switch in the home.

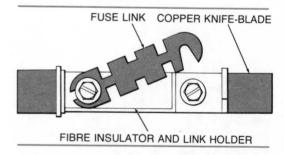

FUSE LINK   COPPER KNIFE-BLADE

FIBRE INSULATOR AND LINK HOLDER

Figure 3.6   100 A knife-blade fuse link

Time-Delay Fuses. Other over-current devices that are used are the time-delay fuses, commonly known as *fusetrons* or *fustats*. They are time-lag fuses. In other words, they *do not blow* like ordinary fuses on large but temporary loads, but they *do blow* on continuous overloads or short circuits. The best application for this type of fuse is on motor circuits. (See Figure 3.7)

Figure 3.7   **Time-delay fusetron or fustat**

Circuit Breaker. A circuit breaker is an over-current device which looks like an ordinary toggle switch. A toggle switch is the type of switch used in your home for lighting circuits. It snaps up and down. The circuit breaker acts in the same way as a time-delay fuse except that when it trips on an overload or short circuit it can be reset. This is an advantage over the time-delay type because a spare fuse is not always available. Circuit breakers are rated in amperes just as fuses are. They are especially good for motor circuit protection.

Fuse Safety Rules

Fuses will protect electrical circuits if they are used in the correct manner. For your personal safety, follow the safety rules listed below:

1. Do not replace a fuse of the proper size and rating with one that is larger in size or rating.
2. Do not attempt to repair a blown plug fuse.
3. Do not insert a coin or any other metal in a fuse socket.
4. Before replacing a fuse turn off the main fuse switch if possible.
5. When replacing a fuse always stand on a dry surface. Do not touch any wet surfaces or metal pipes.
6. When replacing a fuse be sure the fuse is screwed tightly into the socket.

For Review

1. What causes heat in a conductor when current flows through it?
2. What is the purpose of a fuse in a circuit?
3. How are fuses connected in a circuit?
4. What is the composition of the fuse link?
5. What causes the link in a fuse to melt?
6. Why must fuses of higher rating than the capacity of the conductors in the circuit *never* be inserted?
7. Name three types of fuses.
8. State the current rating of each type of fuse.
9. Where is each type of fuse used?
10. Why are fuse links enclosed?
11. Name the size and type of fuse used on branch lighting circuits in a homes.
12. Name the size and type of fuse used (a) for ranges (b) for the main services (c) for automobiles.
13. What are time-delay fuses?
14. Where are time-delay fuses mostly used?
15. What materials are used in the making of plug fuses?
16. How are circuit breakers rated?
17. What causes an overload?
18. How can you tell if a plug fuse is blown?
19. What governs the size of fuse for a circuit?

Incandescent Lamps

The heating effect of an electric current is used to advantage in the electric lamp. The lamp operates on the principle of heating a wire to a white heat. This heat, called *incandescence,* is what produces light.

The filament is made of *tungsten.* Tungsten, a high resistance material, has a very high melting point. To keep the tungsten from burning, it is placed in a glass bulb. All the air is drawn out of the bulb through the exhaust tube and an inert gas, such as argon or nitrogen, is inserted. This gas prevents the oxidation of the filament. The filament is suspended on supports and the ends are brought out to the base which is designed for ease in changing a lamp. Figure 3.8 illustrates an incandescent lamp.

Lamps are made in various sizes, voltages, and wattage ratings. Some

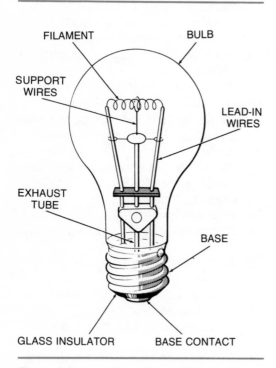

Figure 3.8   **Incandescent lamp**

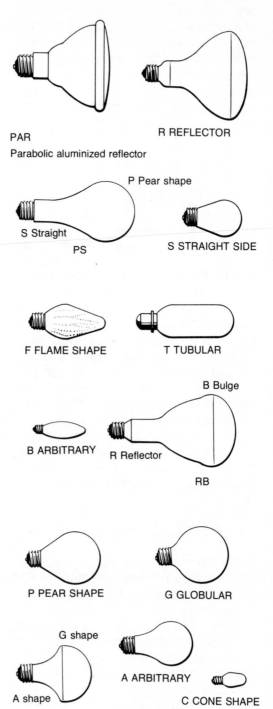

Figure 3.9   **Various types of incandescent lamps**

Introductory Electricity

lamps are clear and others may be inside frosted to prevent glare. Voltage ratings may vary from 1.5 V to 240 V and the wattage may vary from 7 W to 1500 W. Lamps may have different bases, such as the standard medium base shown in Figure 3.8, the bayonet types used in flashlights, or the mogul base used in trilite lamps.

Figure 3.9 shows a very limited number of types of incandescent lamps and their shapes.

Figure 3.10 shows the common types of lamp bases.

Other types of lamps and lamp bases are shown in Figure 3.11. These are special application lamps and are widely used for industrial and commercial work.

BAYONET

CANDELABRA

INTERMEDIATE

MEDIUM

ADMEDIUM

MOGUL

Figure 3.10   **Common types of lamp bases**

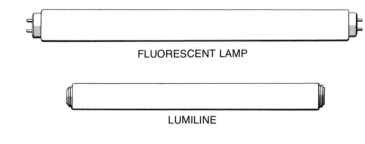
FLUORESCENT LAMP

LUMILINE

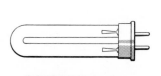
GERMICIDAL LAMP

Used to eliminate microorganisms
(sterilization of doctors' and
dentists' instruments)

OZONE-PRODUCING LAMP

Used to combat unpleasant odours
commonly encountered in homes, offices,
storage cabinets, lockers, and the like

Figure 3.11   **Examples of specialty lamps**

For Review

1. What "effect" is used in the electric lamp?
2. Upon what principle does the lamp operate?
3. What is the filament made of?
4. Why is this filament used in an incandescent lamp?
5. What keeps the filament from burning out?
6. Why is argon or nitrogen gas inserted in the bulb?
7. Name three types of lamp bases.
8. What are two common voltage and wattage ratings of lamps used in your home?
9. What type of base is used on a flashlight lamp?
10. What type of base is used on a trilite lamp?
11. (a) Name three other types of lamps.
    (b) Where would these lamps mostly be used?
12. Why are lamps inside frosted?

4

Magnetism

To understand electricity one must be familiar with magnetism. *Magnetism* is defined as the property that a body has of attracting iron, steel, or other "magnetic" materials. Although the exact nature of this force of attraction is unknown, its effects can be observed, measured, and analyzed.

There are two theories of magnetism. One is known as *Weber's Molecular Theory of Magnetism* and the other is the *Domain Electron Theory.* These will be covered later in this section.

Magnetism was first discovered in Asia Minor about 4000 years ago. The people noticed that certain black rocks possessed the property of attracting iron. These rocks were named "magnets" after a nearby city, Magnesia. This black rock has also been called lodestone but is now known as magnetic oxide of iron, or magnetite. (See Figure 4.1)

Figure 4.1   Natural magnet (lodestone)

Magnetic Substance

Any material that is either attracted or repelled by a magnet is said to be *magnetic material.* Iron and steel are highly magnetic and are ordinarily used for commercial purposes rather than other magnetic materials. Cobalt and nickel also have a small amount of magnetic properties. Alnico (an alloy of aluminum, nickel, and cobalt) is the most powerful magnetic substance known. A *non-magnetic material* is any substance which is not attracted by a magnet.

Types of Magnets

There are two types of magnets: *natural* and *artificial.* Lodestone is an iron ore and is termed a natural magnet. Artificial magnets are manufactured magnets, such as bar magnets and horseshoe magnets. These are classed as *permanent magnets.* Figures 4.2 and 4.3 show these magnets with their magnetic fields.

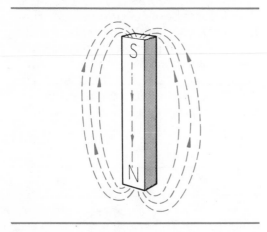

Figure 4.2   Bar magnet

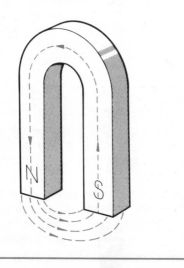

Figure 4.3   Horseshoe magnet

Another type of artificial magnet is the *electromagnet.* This is made by winding a few turns of insulated wire around an iron bar and passing an electrical current through the wire. This is termed a *temporary magnet.* Electromagnets will be covered in a later section of the course.

Induced and Residual Magnetism

The area of attraction surrounding a magnet is known as its *magnetic field.* A bar of iron located in this magnetic field will itself become magnetized. This is known as *induced magnetism.* (See Figure 4.4) When the iron bar is removed from the vicinity of the first magnet, it will retain a certain amount of residual magnetism. *Residual magnetism* is the magnetism that remains in the iron after the magnetizing force has been removed. The amount of residual magnetism depends on the type of iron in the bar. Hard steel has greater retentivity than either soft iron or soft steel. Thus, hard steel or a nickel-iron alloy is used in the manufacture of permanent magnets.

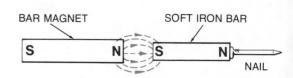

Figure 4.4   Induced magnetism

Permeability

The ease with which a material will allow magnetic lines of force to pass through it is called *permeability.*
NOTE: Soft iron is very easy to magnetize and is said to have high

permeability. Hard steel is very difficult to magnetize and is said to have low permeability.

Originally, magnets were produced by stroking a bar of iron or steel lengthwise with a piece of magnetite. (See Figure 4.5) Now the magnetic properties of an electric current are used to magnetize the iron. This will be described in the section on Electromagnetism.

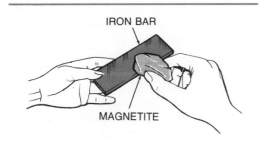

Figure 4.5   Stroking a bar of iron with magnetite to produce a magnet

Poles

When a magnet is suspended from a string at its mid-point and is free to turn, as in Figure 4.6, it will come to rest in a specific position. In this position, one

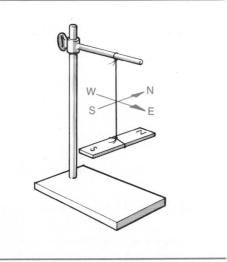

Figure 4.6   Suspended bar magnet

particular end will always point toward the north. To identify it, this *north-seeking* end is stamped "N" and is called the *north pole* of the magnet. The opposite end is stamped "S" and is called the *south pole.*

Attraction and Repulsion

When the north pole of a second bar magnet is brought close to the north pole of the suspended magnet (see Figure 4.7) the suspended north pole will turn away. If the north pole of the second magnet approaches the south pole of the suspended magnet, the latter will swing toward it. This experiment demonstrates the *First Law of Magnetism.*

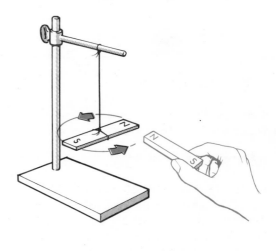

Figure 4.7   Suspended bar magnet

First Law of Magnetism

(a) *Like magnetic poles repel each other.*
(b) *Unlike magnetic poles attract each other.*

This explains why the suspended magnet in Figure 4.6 lines up in the north-south direction. It has been found that the earth itself is a large magnet with a "south" pole located about 1600 km (kilometres) from the geographical North Pole. Thus the north pole of a suspended bar magnet or compass needle is always attracted in a northerly direction. (See Figure 4.8)

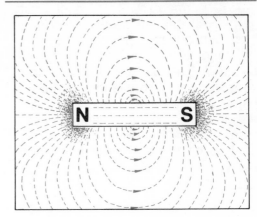

Figure 4.9   Magnetic lines around a bar magnet

The lines of force that come from the north pole of one magnet move through the air to the south pole of the second magnet, as shown in Figure 4.10. The lines of force pass through the second magnet, through the air, and finally return to the south pole of the first magnet.

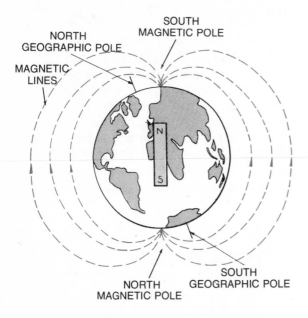

Figure 4.8   The earth as a huge magnet

Magnetic Fields

Iron filings sprinkled on a cardboard covering a bar magnet will take up the pattern shown in Figure 4.9 if the cardboard is gently tapped. This pattern is characteristic of all bar magnets. It shows the direction and intensity of the *lines of force* in the magnet. Note that the greatest concentration of filings is at the poles where the *magnetic intensity* is greatest. Each iron filing when placed in a magnetic field becomes a small magnet itself. Thus the filings "line up" in accordance with the First Law of Magnetism along the lines of force which are said to "flow" from the north pole to the south. These lines of force are sometimes referred to as *magnetic flux.*

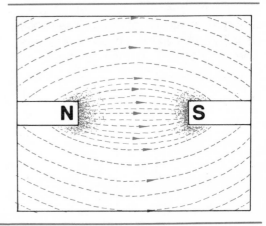

Figure 4.10   Magnetic lines between unlike poles

When a north pole of one magnet is placed near the north pole of another, the magnets will repel each other. The lines of force may be represented by the iron filings as shown in Figure 4.11.

Introductory Electricity

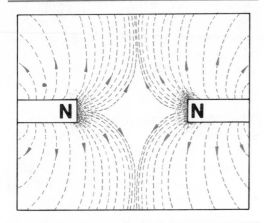

Figure 4.11 Magnetic lines between like poles

Notice that the lines of force are crowded together; this explains the repelling action. Notice, also, that the lines of force do not intersect.

Figures 4.10 and 4.11 illustrate facts which have already been stated, namely:

Unlike poles attract; like poles repel.

Second Law of Magnetism

The attraction or repulsion between two magnets will be greatest when they are closest to each other and will be weakest when they are farthest apart. Stated as the Second Law of Magnetism:

(a) *As the distance between two magnets decreases, the attraction or repulsion increases.*

(b) *As the distance between two magnets increases, the attraction or repulsion decreases.*

Direction of Magnetic Lines

The magnetic field around a bar magnet is more clearly shown in Figure 4.12. By placing small compasses in various parts of the field, it is seen that the magnetic lines have a definite direction. The end of the magnet from which the lines leave is known as the north pole and the end of the magnet to which the lines return is known as the south pole. A horseshoe magnet may be plotted in the same manner.

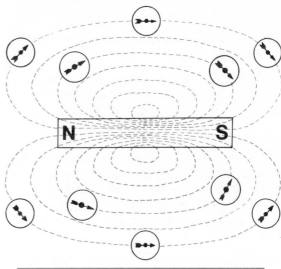

Figure 4.12 Magnetic lines plotted with a compass

Weber's Molecular Theory of Magnetism

Weber's theory was devised in relation to chemistry, but it serves as an explanation for the laws of magnetism. It states that every material is composed of minute particles called *molecules*. In any magnetic material, each molecule is a magnet with a north and south pole. Before the material is magnetized the molecules lie in a haphazard manner (see Figure 4.13), but after being magnetized the molecules lie in an orderly fashion (see Figure 4.14).

Figure 4.13 Molecular arrangement before magnetizing

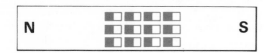

Figure 4.14   Molecular arrangement after magnetizing

NOTE: All the north poles lie in one direction and all the south poles
lie in the opposite direction, as
in Figure 4.14.

Further proof of this theory can be
shown by magnetizing a hacksaw blade
and then breaking the blade into as
many pieces as possible. (See Figure
4.15) Notice that each piece becomes a
small magnet and has a definite north
pole and south pole.

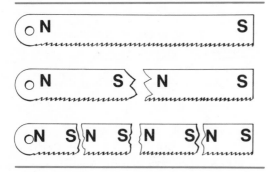

Figure 4.15   Each piece of steel becomes a magnet

Domain Theory

The Domain Theory of magnetism assumes that each *electron* in a material is
a magnet in itself. The orbits of the electrons in each atom of an unmagnetized
iron bar are different at any given instant;
hence, the forces caused by each electron cancel the forces of other electrons.
As a result, there is no outside magnetic
influence.

When an iron bar is magnetized the
electron orbits are aligned and syn-

chronized so that the circles of force
combine to produce a strong bar magnet whose magnetic influence is readily
detectable.

Demagnetizing Magnets

When magnets are subjected to considerable jarring or vibration, they lose
some of their magnetism. This jarring
loosens the molecules from their orderly
pattern, thus weakening the magnet.
Heating a magnet will also cause the
magnet to lose strength.

Consequent Poles

Sometimes a bar of steel will have more
than two poles. (See Figure 4.16) The extra pole between the two poles is called
a *consequent pole.* Observe that each
line of force forms a closed loop.

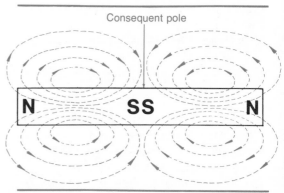

Figure 4.16   Consequent pole magnet

Storage of Magnets

The simple bar magnet is used princi-
pally for experimental purposes and has
very little practical value. Since the magnetic lines must travel a comparatively
long distance through the air, bar magnets are never very strong. When not in
use, bar magnets should be kept in
pairs (see Figure 4.17), and horseshoe
magnets require a soft-iron "keeper"
(see Figure 4.18).

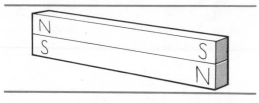

Figure 4.17   Storage of bar magnets

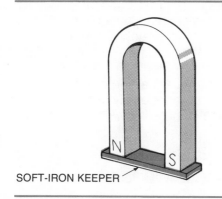

SOFT-IRON KEEPER

Figure 4.18   Storage of horseshoe magnet

Ring Magnets (Toroids)

The ring magnet has little external magnetic effect. Since the magnetic lines are contained within the metal of the ring, no external poles are produced. (See Figure 4.19) Ring magnets are used as cores for special transformers.

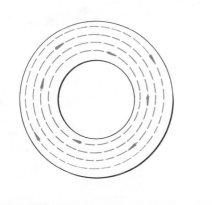

Figure 4.19   Ring magnet—no external poles

If a section of the ring is removed, a magnet is formed. (See Figure 4.20) A definite north pole and south pole are produced. This form of magnet is very strong since the air gap is too small to hinder seriously the flow of the magnetic lines.

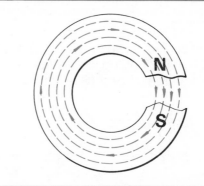

Figure 4.20   Broken ring magnet shows definite north pole and south pole

Laminated Magnets

The laminated or compound magnet (Figure 4.21) is more powerful in proportion to its mass than a solid magnet of the same size. This type of magnet is made of sections of steel fastened together with all like poles at one end. Laminated magnets of the horseshoe type are used in ignition magnets and telephone magnets.

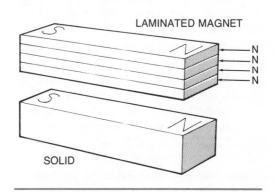

LAMINATED MAGNET

N
N
N
N

SOLID

Figure 4.21   Magnet comparison

Magnetic Screens (Shielding)

There is no known substance that can prevent magnetic lines from passing through itself. The lines pass easily through glass, wood, copper, and other materials. It is occasionally necessary to shield electrical instruments from the earth's magnetic field and other magnetic effects. The shielding effect is brought about by surrounding the instrument with a soft-iron screen. (See Figure 4.22)

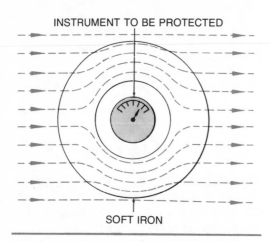

INSTRUMENT TO BE PROTECTED

SOFT IRON

Figure 4.22 Magnetic lines by-pass the instrument

NOTE: The amount of resistance or opposition a material offers to the flow of magnetic lines is called *reluctance.* Magnetic lines will flow much more easily through a magnetic material than through a non-magnetic material. Therefore, magnetic materials have low reluctance and non-magnetic materials have high reluctance. *All non-magnetic materials have the same reluctance as air.*

Since iron is a much better conductor of magnetic lines than air, the lines that would ordinarily pass through the space to be protected are by-passed through the iron. Expensive watches carried in electric power plants are usu-ally kept in soft-iron cases to protect the steel parts from becoming magnetized. If a watch is magnetized it will lose time.

Characteristics of Lines of Force

1. They do not cross each other.
2. They always form closed loops.
3. They act like stretched rubber bands.
4. They have polarity.
5. They penetrate all materials.
6. They flow more easily through magnetic materials.

Compass (Magnetic Needle)

The magnetic compass shown in Figure 4.23 is an instrument used to determine geographical direction. It also has many important laboratory uses. It is simply a delicate bar magnet accurately balanced and suspended so that it may rotate freely on a pivot. The north pole points in the direction of the magnetic flux. The compass needle is a very convenient device for determining whether

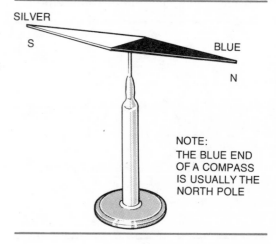

SILVER

S

BLUE

N

NOTE:
THE BLUE END
OF A COMPASS
IS USUALLY THE
NORTH POLE

Figure 4.23 Magnetic compass or magnetic needle

Introductory Electricity

or not a piece of iron or steel is magnetized. It is used to determine direction and polarity.

Dipping Needle

A magnetic needle freely suspended so that it can rotate in a *vertical* plane is called a *dipping needle* (Figure 4.24). At the magnetic north pole, the needle would be vertical and the south end of the needle would point downward. At the magnetic south pole, the needle would also be vertical but the south end of the needle would point upward. At the magnetic equator, the needle would be horizontal because the earth's magnetic forces are balanced.

The angle which the lines of force make with the earth's surface is called the *angle of dip*.

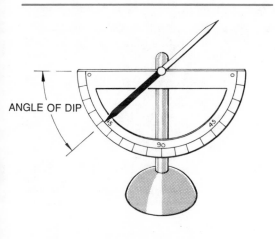

Figure 4.24   Dipping needle

The Magic Link

You may be wondering what all this has to do with electricity and electric power. This will become clearer as you proceed through the discussion on electromagnetism and electromagnetic induction. In the meantime it may be helpful to remember that iron and the magnetic properties of iron are essential to the operation of every electric generator, transformer, and motor in use today.

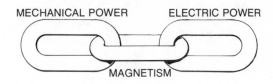

Figure 4.25   The magic link

Uses for Permanent Magnets

1. dc generators
2. dc motors
3. Relays
4. Electrical meters
5. Radio loudspeakers
6. Telephone receivers
7. Microphones
8. Phonograph pickups
9. Compass needles
10. Tack hammers
11. Speedometers and tachometers
12. Magnetic chucks
13. Magnetic jigs
14. Magnetic separators
15. Coin separators in vending machines
16. Clocks
17. Hearing aids
18. Voltage regulators
19. Magnetic doors
20. Door locks

Summary of Important Magnetic Terms

1. *Lodestone:* A piece of magnetite, a naturally magnetic iron ore
2. *Poles:* The two regions of greatest flux concentration of a magnet

3. *Polarity:* The characteristic of having magnetic poles or electric charges
4. *Magnetic Lines:* Imaginary lines which make up a magnetic field
5. *Flux:* Magnetic lines of force
6. *Magnetic Field:* The area around a magnetic pole where magnetic force exists
7. *North Pole:* The pole at which the magnetic force leaves the magnet
8. *South Pole:* The pole at which the magnetic force re-enters the magnet
9. *Temporary Magnet:* Magnets which lose their magnetism after a short time (seconds, minutes), as in electromagnets
10. *Permanent Magnet:* Magnets which retain their magnetism for a long time (years)
11. *Magnetic Materials:* Materials which can be magnetized; high permeability substances
12. *Non-magnetic Materials:* Materials which cannot be magnetized; high reluctance substances
13. *Magnetic Circuit:* The complete path followed by magnetic lines of force
14. *Induction:* Realignment of molecules in magnetic substances to produce a magnet
15. *Retentivity:* The ability of a material to retain its magnetism after the magnetization has been removed
16. *Residual Magnetism:* The magnetism left in a magnet after magnetization has been removed
17. *Permeability:* The ease with which a material allows magnetic lines of force to pass through it
18. *Reluctance:* The amount of resistance or opposition offered to the passage of magnetic lines of force
19. *Compass:* A magnet free to turn
20. *Consequent Pole Magnet:* A magnet which has like poles at the ends and an unlike pole in the centre
21. *Ring Magnet:* A permanent magnet shaped into a ring. The magnetic force is contained within the ring and there are no external parts

For Review

1. What is the name given to the substance that is naturally magnetic?
2. What is meant by (a) a magnetic material, (b) a non-magnetic material?
3. Name two elementary substances, other than steel and iron, which exhibit strong magnetic effects.
4. What are the three types of artificial magnets?
5. Why will magnetic lines of force pass freely through soft iron?
6. What is residual magnetism?
7. Why does steel make a more permanent magnet than soft iron?
8. If a piece of soft iron were held between the poles of a horseshoe magnet, what would be the polarity of the end of the soft iron at which the lines enter?
9. What is the First Law of Magnetism?
10. Name two methods for magnetizing a piece of steel.
11. What is meant by polarity?
12. State the Second Law of Magnetism.
13. What is reluctance in a magnetic circuit?
14. If a bar magnet is cut into several pieces, what will be the result?
15. Explain the molecular theory of magnetism.
16. What effect will the following have on a magnet: (a) excessive heat (b) striking the magnet?
17. Make a sketch showing the magnetic field of force around a bar magnet with north poles at the ends and a consequent pole in the centre.
18. What are the advantages of laminated magnets over a solid piece of steel of the same qualities and size?
19. What type of magnet has no polarity? How can it be made to have polarity?
20. Draw a diagram illustrating the principles of shielding.
21. Sketch three bar magnets arranged in such a manner as to have little or no external field.
22. What is a compass?
23. If you were standing on the magnetic north pole, which way would a compass needle point? Why?
24. What is a practical application for ring magnets?
25. When would the compass needle point in a true horizontal position?
26. What is meant by the angle of dip?
27. You are given two similar bars of steel. One is a magnet. Explain in step form the tests you would make using only the two bars to determine which one is the magnet.
28. Name four important properties that lines of force possess.
29. Name eight practical uses for permanent magnets.

5 The Primary Cell

There are two kinds of battery cells: the *primary* or *dry cell* and the *secondary* or *storage cell.* The first battery cell was made in 1798 by Alessandro Volta and, though it was a crude affair judged by the dry cell of today, it demonstrated the electro-chemical principles underlying all battery practice.

Volta used copper and zinc plates suspended in a dilute acetic acid solution (the *electrolyte*). Electricity was produced through the consumption of the zinc by the acid; the copper underwent no change during the life of the cell. Various improvements followed with the first "dry" cell being produced in 1888. In this cell the zinc was cup-shaped and was used as one of the poles (*electrodes*) and it contained the other elements as well.

Figure 5.1 illustrates a modern dry cell. The zinc is formed in the shape of a

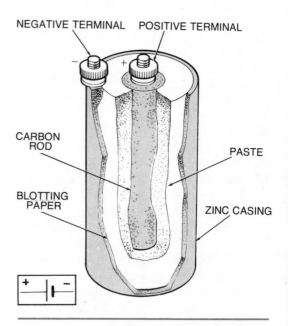

Figure 5.1   **#6 dry cell construction and symbol for single dry cell.**

Battery Cells

can or casing and is lined with a material resembling blotter paper. The zinc casing is also used as a negative pole and is depicted by a negative symbol (—). The central carbon rod is the positive pole and is depicted by a positive symbol (+). The space around and under the carbon rod is filled with a paste consisting of sal ammoniac, zinc chloride, manganese dioxide, and ground carbon.

The sal ammoniac is the electrolyte and the zinc chloride improves the action. The manganese dioxide is used to remove the hydrogen bubbles which otherwise would collect on the carbon and interfere with the chemical action and the production of electricity. The material resembling blotter paper is used to absorb and hold the electrolyte. The cell top is sealed with sealing wax or another compound to retain the moisture in the paste. Without moisture the cell would be useless. The carbon rod and zinc casing are provided with studs and nuts for making the electrical connections to the external circuit. Heavy paper or cardboard forms the outside case. Figure 5.1 also shows the symbol for a single dry cell.

Operation of Primary Cells.   The chemical action makes the carbon rod positively charged and the zinc negatively charged. This creates a potential difference between the electrodes. When a circuit is completed the chemical action maintains the voltage which causes electrons to pass through the circuit from the zinc to the carbon.

The electromotive force *(emf)* of a new cell is about 1.5 V, and its internal resistance is about 0.1 Ω . A #6 cell has a capacity of about 32 A·h when discharged through a 20 Ω resistance. Then the voltage has been reduced by 0.5 V.

Dry cells are not rechargeable and are thrown away when they become inoperative. They will last about a year if not used and kept in a cool place.

Series Cells

Dry cells can be connected in series in which case the voltage is the sum of the separate voltages (Figure 5.2). The schematic symbol for cells in series is shown in Figure 5.3.

Figure 5.2   **Dry cells connected in series**

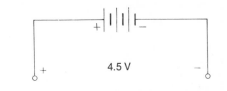

Figure 5.3   **Symbols for cells in series**

This series connection would produce 3 × 1.5 V = 4.5 V across the three cells. The ampere-hours remain the same as for one cell, that is, 32 A·h.

Parallel Cells

Dry cells can be connected in parallel if more current is required than can be provided by one cell and only 1.5 V are needed. Figure 5.4 shows three dry cells connected in parallel. This connection would produce 3 × 32 A·h = 96 A·h.

The voltage remains the same as for one cell, that is, 1.5 V. The symbol for dry cells connected in parallel is shown in Figure 5.5.

Figure 5.4   Dry cells connected in parallel

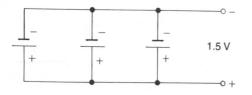

1.5 V

Figure 5.5   Symbols for cells in parallel

+Series-Parallel Cells

If a higher voltage is required, as well as a greater current, a series-parallel circuit may be advisable. Figure 5.6 shows two sets of three cells connected in series and the two sets are connected in parallel. This connection would produce 3×1.5 V $= 4.5$ V and 2×32 A·h $= 64$ A·h. Figure 5.7 shows the symbol for dry cells connected in series parallel.

Figure 5.6   Dry cells connected in series-parallel

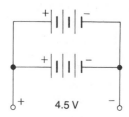

4.5 V

Figure 5.7   Symbols for cells in series-parallel

NOTE: The number of cells in each set or *bank* must be the same or the higher voltage set will discharge into the lower one. In other words, the smaller set will act as a load to the larger set rather than as a parallel device. For the same reason, it is inadvisable to put a set of new cells in parallel with a set of old cells.

NOTE: The term battery is sometimes used incorrectly when the meaning intended is cell. A *battery* is a group of cells connected in series, parallel, or a combination of series-parallel.

Common Types of Primary Cells

Some of the more common or popular types of 1.5 V dry cells are the #6, D, C, AA, and pen-light. (Figure 5.8)

Another common dry cell battery is the 9 V transistor type. This battery has flat wafer-type dry cells tightly pressed together. A special conducting material (silver wax) connects the individual cells to form the series connection. Figure 5.10 shows a 9 V transistor battery.

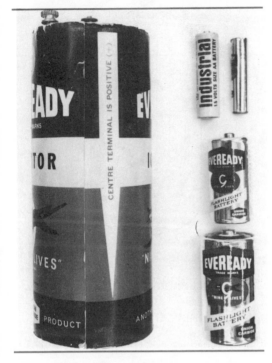

Figure 5.8   Popular dry cells

Figure 5.10   9 V transistor battery

Uses of the Primary Cell

The smaller dry cells are used in pen-lights, flashlights, transistor radios, hearing aids, telephones, and in many of the communication media. The larger cells are used in bell-and-buzzer circuits, test-ringing circuits, and communication circuits.

Figure 5.9 shows the more popular 1.5 V dry cells with actual dimensions and their capacities in ampere-hours.

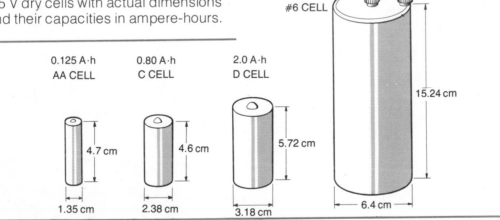

Figure 5.9   1.5 V dry cells and their actual dimensions

For Review

1. Name two types of battery cells.
2. From which terminal does the current flow?
3. What are the four chemicals used to form the paste?
4. How much *emf* does a dry cell develop?
5. Would a dry cell produce a higher *emf* if the size of the electrodes were made larger? Explain.
6. Name three electrical apparatuses that make use of dry cells.
7. Why is it undesirable to connect cells in a series-parallel combination when one set is at a higher voltage rating?
8. How are dry cells connected in order to increase the voltage?
9. How are dry cells connected in order to increase the ampere-hour rating?
10. How are dry cells connected in order to increase both the voltage and ampere-hour rating?

11. Name the parts of the dry cell corresponding to the numbers shown in Figure 5.11.

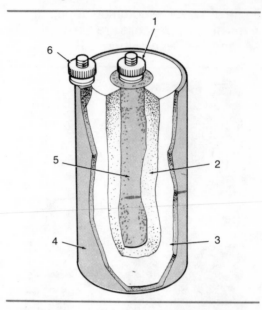

Figure 5.11

12. Make a schematic drawing to show how a #6 dry cell would be connected to obtain 9 V and a 64 A·h capacity.

6

Magnetism produced by an electric current is known as *electromagnetism.* Electromagnetism is essential to the operation of electric generators, motors, and transformers. Usually this electric current flows in a wire coil surrounding an iron core.

The discovery that magnetism existed as the result of a current flowing was made about 1820 by a Danish physicist, Hans Christian Oersted. He suspended a magnetic needle above a wire. The wire was turned to lie along the needle in a north-south direction. When he passed a current through the wire from the south to the north, the north pole of the magnetic needle moved to a westerly direction (Figure 6.1). This indicated to him that the current was producing a magnetic influence on the needle.

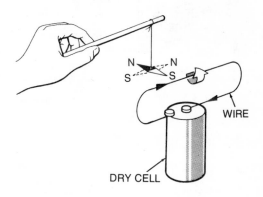

Figure 6.1   Electric current affects a magnetic needle

He then placed the needle below the wire and the north pole turned to an easterly direction. By other similar experiments he verified that the direction

Electro-
magnetism

of current flow determined the way the magnetic lines moved around a current-carrying conductor.

Further evidence of the presence of magnetism around a current-carrying wire was found by the attraction the wire had for iron filings. They would adhere to the wire until the current was interrupted (Figure 6.2). This is explained by the preference for magnetism to take a path through the iron rather than through the air, and because the density of the magnetic lines is greatest closest to the wire.

Figure 6.2   Current-carrying wire produces magnetism

Magnetic Lines Around Conductors

The flux or magnetic lines of force surrounding a current-carrying conductor can be studied by passing the wire vertically through a horizontal cardboard. Iron filings sprinkled on the cardboard will take up the concentric circle pattern shown in Figure 6.3. This indicates that the magnetic lines of force form continuous concentric circles around the wire. This pattern is the same anywhere along the length of the wire. A heavy current will produce strong lines of force extend-

ing some distance out from the wire. A small current will produce weaker lines of force affecting only those filings close to the wire. In either case, the magnetizing force is strongest right at the wire and weakest farthest away from the wire.

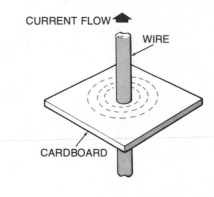

Figure 6.3   Iron filings indicate flux pattern

By placing small magnetic compasses on the cardboard, it can be shown that the magnetic flux has direction as well as magnitude. As soon as current flows the needles of the compasses arrange themselves in a clockwise or counter-clockwise direction around the conductor, as in Figure 6.4.

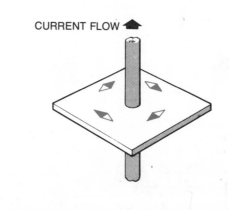

Figure 6.4   Compasses show flux direction

If the direction of the current is reversed, the magnetic compass needles reverse. (Figure 6.5). Thus a magnetic field around a conductor can be established in either direction by controlling the direction of the current flow.

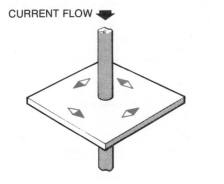

CURRENT FLOW

Figure 6.5   Current reversed—flux reversed

The Left-Hand Rule

The *Left-Hand Rule* is a handy method for determining the direction of flux if the current direction is known (Figure 6.6). When the conductor is grasped in the left hand with the thumb pointing in the direction of current flow, the fingers point in the direction of the flux. This rule should be memorized.

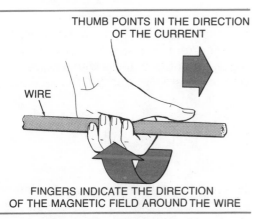

THUMB POINTS IN THE DIRECTION OF THE CURRENT

WIRE

FINGERS INDICATE THE DIRECTION OF THE MAGNETIC FIELD AROUND THE WIRE

Figure 6.6   Left-hand rule for current-carrying conductor

Remember these three points:
1. Use the *left hand*.
2. The *thumb* indicates *current direction*.
3. The *fingers* indicate *flux direction*.

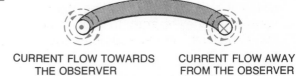

CURRENT FLOW TOWARDS THE OBSERVER   CURRENT FLOW AWAY FROM THE OBSERVER

Figure 6.7   Magnetic field around a current-carrying conductor

Magnetic Polarity of a Coil

A straight current-carrying conductor, such as the one in Figure 6.6, has no poles in the sense that a bar magnet has poles. Under the section on magnetism, poles were described as places at which magnetism was concentrated and where the lines of flux emerged from or re-entered the magnet (Figure 6.8).

In the case of a straight conductor, these points do not exist.

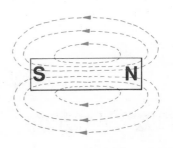

Figure 6.8   Flux lines around a bar magnet

If the straight conductor is arranged in a coil, the coil takes on the properties of a magnet (Figure 6.9). The concentric lines of flux around the wire combine to produce a magnetic field around and through the entire coil. These lines emerge from one end of the coil thus giving it the properties of a north pole. They re-enter the coil at the other end which then becomes a south pole.

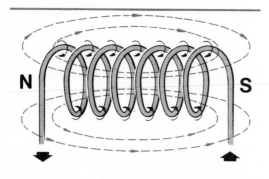

Figure 6.9   A wire coil or "solenoid"

NOTE: The polarity may be reversed by winding the coil in the opposite direction or by reversing the current through the coil.

Left-Hand Rule for Coils

The Left-Hand Rule may be applied to a coil (Figure 6.10). Grasp the coil with the left hand so that the fingers go around the coil in the direction of current flow; the thumb will then point to the north end of the coil.

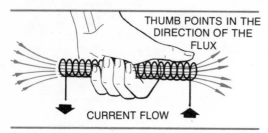

THUMB POINTS IN THE DIRECTION OF THE FLUX

CURRENT FLOW

Figure 6.10   Left-hand rule for current-carrying coil

Ampere-Turns

The wire coil, or *solenoid*, (Figure 6.11) can be used to attract and pick up iron just as a bar magnet can. It will be found that the amount of iron that can be attracted will depend on:
1. The amount of current in the coil *(I)*
2. The number of turns in the coil *(N)*
3. The type of core material
4. The area of the core

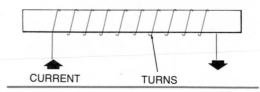

CURRENT   TURNS

Figure 6.11   Wire coil with current flowing (ampere-turns)

For a particular iron-core electromagnet it can be shown that the magnetic strength varies directly as the product of the current (amperes) and the number of turns. Thus the magnetizing force can be expressed in terms of *ampere-turns* as follows:

Ampere-turns = current in amperes
$\times$ number of turns
= IN
= magnetomotive force (magnetizing force)

The same magnetizing force can be obtained by using a few turns with a large current, Figure 6.12, or by using a great number of turns with a correspondingly smaller current, Figure 6.13.

Left-Hand Rule for Electromagnets

Grasp the electromagnet with the *left hand*, fingers pointing in the direction of the current flow. Extend the thumb and it will point to the north pole (Figure 6.14).

Introductory Electricity

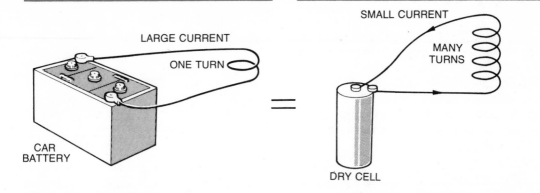

Figure 6.12 Heavy current times one turn

Figure 6.13 Light current times many turns

Uses of Electromagnetism

Electromagnetism is used directly in the electrical industry in many ways. Most applications involve the use of iron cores to intensify the magnetic effect. Soft iron is used for the cores of electromagents because it has a retentivity which is lower than that of hard steel. A few of the many applications of electromagnetism are listed below:

1. Lifting magnets for scrap iron
2. Motor starters and controls
3. Door bells, buzzers, chimes
4. Relays
5. Telegraph keys and sounders
6. Telephone receivers
7. Measuring instruments
8. Electrical machinery
9. Circuit breakers
10. Brakes for hoists on cranes
11. Magnetic chucks
12. Magnetic clutches
13. Radio loudspeakers

In addition, the field poles of electric generators and motors are electromagnets. You will undoubtedly see many of these in your everyday life. Figure 6.15 shows two applications of electromagnets.

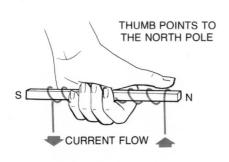

Figure 6.14 Left-hand rule for electromagnets

Figure 6.15 Vibrating bell and motor

For Review

1. What is electromagnetism?
2. How does a magnetic field arrange itself around a conductor?
3. Sketch the magnetic field around a current-carrying conductor.
4. If the current is reversed through a conductor, what happens to the magnetic field?
5. State the Left-Hand Rule for determining the flux direction in a current-carrying conductor.
6. How can the magnetic field be increased?
7. State the rule by which the polarity of an electromagnet is determined when the direction of current is known.
8. Sketch the connections of an electromagnet connected so that it will have a south pole at each end.
9. What are the polarity and name of the pole in the centre of the electromagnet in question 8?
10. State the four factors which determine the strength of an electromagnet.
11. Name six practical uses for electromagnets.
12. Draw the magnetic field of an air-core electromagnet.
13. What are the advantages of electromagnets over permanent magnets?
14. Which electromagnet will have the greater strength: one with 10 turns carrying a current of 2 A or one with 5 turns carrying 5 A?

7

Relays

A *relay* is a magnetically operated switch. (See Figure 7.1). It operates by the attraction of an armature to an electromagnet. Figure 7.2 shows the operation of a simple relay.

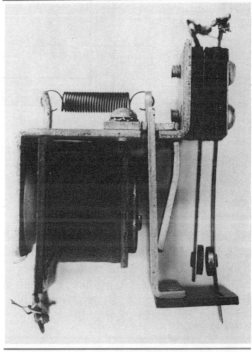

Figure 7.1   Simple relay

When the switch is closed, current will flow through the coil to produce the electromagnet. The electromagnet attracts the armature which closes the circuit to the lamp. When the switch is opened, the electromagnet is de-energized and the spring will pull the armature back and open the circuit.

The use of a relay makes it possible to control a circuit from a distance and to control large amounts of currents with smaller currents. Relays are used in remote lighting circuits, motor control, automobile starters, telegraph circuits, and as safety controls in oil furnaces and fire alarm systems.

Relays and Circuit Breakers

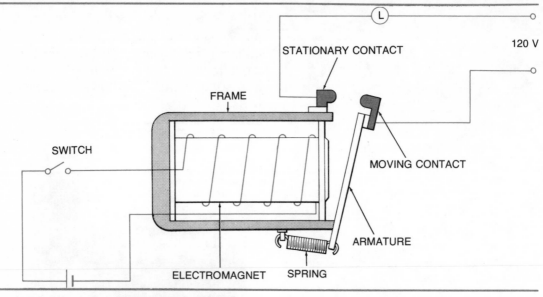

Figure 7.2   Operation of magnetic relay

Circuit Breaker

A *circuit breaker* is an over-current device which looks similar to an ordinary toggle switch. A *toggle switch* is the type of switch used in lighting circuits in the home which snaps up and down.

The circuit breaker acts as a time-delay fuse, except that when it trips on an overload or short circuit it can be reset. This is an advantage over the time-delay type because a spare fuse may not always be available. Circuit breakers are rated in amperes as are fuses. They are especially good for motor circuit protection. Circuit breakers are a combination switch and safety device. Figure 7.3 shows a circuit breaker.

Figure 7.3   Circuit breaker

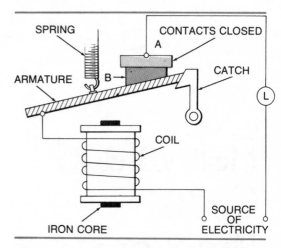

Figure 7.4   Operation of magnetic circuit breaker—contacts closed

Introductory Electricity

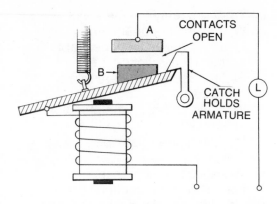

Figure 7.5   Operation of a magnetic circuit breaker—contacts open

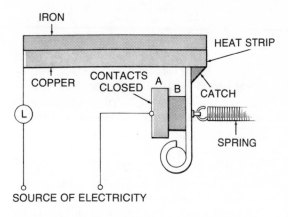

Figure 7.6   Operation of heat strip breaker—contacts closed

The operation of a circuit breaker is shown in Figure 7.4.

When the circuit is closed, the current will flow from the source, through the coil, the armature, the closed contacts "A" and "B", the lamp and return to the source, completing the circuit.

If an overload or a short circuit occurs, a greater current will flow from the source. This increased current will increase the magnetic strength of the coil and will attract the armature which will open the contacts "A" and "B" and open the circuit, thus preventing any damage to the devices that are connected to the circuit. (See Figure 7.5). The armature which is under tension by the spring is held by the catch and remains there until it is reset. After the circuit breaker is reset, the contacts will close to complete the circuit.

Heat Strip Breaker

The heat strip or bi-metal strip breaker uses a strip made of two different kinds of metal, either welded or riveted together.

NOTE: All metals will expand and lengthen when heated. How-

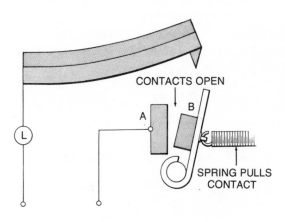

Figure 7.7   Operation of heat strip breaker—contacts open

ever, soft metals will expand at a faster rate than hard metals. Copper, being softer than iron, will expand and lengthen before the iron. When the two are riveted or welded to form a strip, with the iron above the copper as in Figure 7.6, and the strip is heated, the strip will tend to bend upwards. If the copper is above the iron, the strip will bend downwards.

The operation of this circuit breaker is shown in Figure 7.7.

When the circuit is closed, current flows from the source, through the contact points "A" and "B", through the heat strip, through the lamp and returns to the source, completing the circuit.

If an overload or a short circuit occurs, a large current flows. This large current causes the heat strip to become hot and expand upward, as in Figure 7.7, opening the contacts at "A" and "B", thus opening the circuit to the lamp. Only when the strip has cooled can the breaker be reset on the catch and the circuit be allowed to close.

The amount of current necessary to open the contacts depends on the design of the heat strip.

For Review

1. What is a relay?
2. What is the important feature of relays that makes them desirable in certain types of circuits?
3. State four places where relays may be used.
4. What is the basic principle involved in a relay?
5. Explain how a relay operates. (Use a sketch.)
6. What is a circuit breaker?
7. Name two types of circuit breakers.
8. How is a circuit breaker reset after it has opened the circuit?
9. How is a heat strip constructed? State the principle of operation.
10. Explain how a magnetic circuit breaker operates. (Use a sketch.)
11. What is the moving part of a magnetic breaker called?
12. How is a circuit breaker rated?
13. For what applications are circuit breakers best suited?
14. (a) What are the advantages of circuit breakers over fuses?
    (b) What are the disadvantages?

8

Conductors
and
Connections

Electrical Safety

Electricity can be dangerous and, in some cases, fatal. It must be handled with extreme caution. Even a small electric shock can be very painful, and a standard 120 V outlet in your home is capable of causing a severe shock.

    The principal factor that determines whether you will get a mild or severe shock is the *resistance of your body.* Your body resistance varies. If your body is relatively dry, the resistance will be high and thus a high voltage is needed to give you a severe shock. If, however, your body is moist the resistance is low and a low voltage can give you a severe shock.

Dangerous Electrical Practice

Because of the many electrical hazards which may exist in the home, the following illustrations are presented so that you will be aware of their presence. The illustrations are intended to be amusing. However, it is hoped that they will drive home the fact that these are dangerous practices and should be avoided at all times.

Electrical Safety Rules

The best safety rule for electrical safety is to *use good common sense.* Some specific rules are:
1. Never attempt to repair electrical equipment if you are not qualified to do so.
2. Replace worn and damaged line cords.
3. Never operate electrical appliances when you are in the bathtub or shower.
4. Do not touch a water pipe and an electrical appliance at the same time.

5. Never change a lamp or fuse or touch electrical appliances while standing on a wet concrete floor. (Use a dry board or wooden chair.)
6. Use only 15 A plug fuses in the fuse distribution panel unless otherwise specified.
7. Do not overload an electrical outlet by plugging too many appliances in the outlet.

Ground all tools unless double insulated. If the tool is equipped with a three-prong plug, it should be plugged into a three-hole electrical receptacle. If the adapter is used to accommodate a two-prong receptacle, the adapter wire must be attached to a *known ground*.

It is poor practice to stand on a damp cellar floor and change a light bulb. Stand on insulating material such as a dry board or a dry magazine. This will prevent you from being grounded.

He's about to tune in his last program. Bathtubs and appliances don't mix.

Do not use a tool with frayed cord. Return it for servicing. Use only heavy-duty CSA-approved extension cords of proper wire size and length.

He suddenly remembers that it is not good practice to hold an appliance which is plugged in and the water tap at the same time.

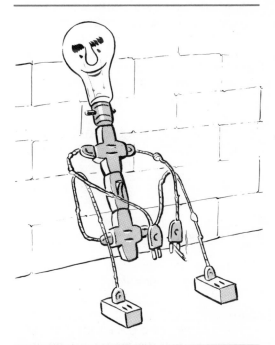

Meet Mr. Skimpy Wiring. Look at the tangle of plugs and sockets. Note the frayed and weak-looking wiring! That's him all right—Skimpy Wiring—the electrical delinquent who is found in 10 000 000 homes. Does he lurk in yours? Have you a toaster that heats slowly? Does your T.V. set "twitch" when other appliances go on? Do fuses blow too often? Beware of the unwanted guest!

Shop Safety Rules

1. Observe all the safety rules and precautions that are listed in your home, when applicable.
2. Do not work on live circuits.
3. Consider every electric circuit as if it were live until proven otherwise.
4. Do not open or close any main switch without permission from the instructor.
5. Never touch a live wire with your bare hands.

Outdoor Safety Rules

1. Never climb high tension towers.
2. Use only electrical hand tools that have grounded outer casings as indicated by a three-prong plug cap.
3. Avoid standing in moist or wet locations while operating electrical hand tools.
4. Avoid standing under a tree during a thunderstorm.
5. Avoid being the highest object outside on a large flat area during a severe thunderstorm.

For Review

1. What are the effects on the human body when it receives (a) mild electric shock (b) a severe electric shock?
2. What is the principal factor that determines the amount of shock that the human body receives? Explain.
3. List five electrical safety rules that should be practiced in the home.
4. List three electrical safety rules that *must* be practiced in the shop.
5. Explain why ungrounded electrical hand tools can be dangerous when operated in wet or moist locations.

Joints and Splices

Before wires are joined, spliced, or connected to terminals, the insulated conductor must be prepared. The insulation must be removed so that the conductor is left bare, clean, and free from cuts or nicks. Conductors improperly skinned may be damaged, resulting in circuit failure at some future date. To insure good electrical and mechanical connections, certain steps should be taken when skinning a conductor.

To Remove Insulation From a Conductor

1. Grasp the conductor firmly.
2. Move the knife away from you.
3. Cut the insulation at an angle, as you would sharpen a pencil.
4. Remove just enough insulation so that the bare conductor is kept to a minimum.

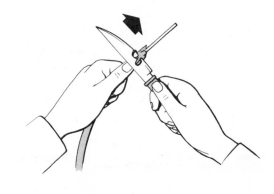

Figure 8.1   Removing insulation

5. Scrape the conductor clean with the knife to remove all the insulation. The result should look like Figure 8.2.

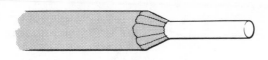

Figure 8.2   Insulation removed

Types of Joints or Splices

Three common electrical joints or splices are used extensively. They are:
1. rat-tail
2. tee or tap
3. Western Union

Rat-tail Splice

The rat-tail splice is used when two or more conductors are joined in places such as boxes or fittings, and when making connections in fixtures. The following is a step procedure for making a rat-tail splice:
1. Remove about 3 cm of the insulation from both conductors.
2. Cross the conductors as in Figure 8.3.

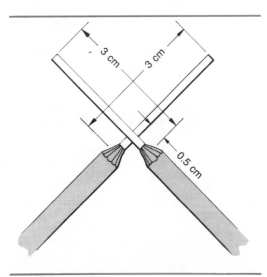

Figure 8.3   Cross conductors

3. Hold both conductors securely with one hand. With a pair of pliers twist the free ends around each other (Figure 8.4).

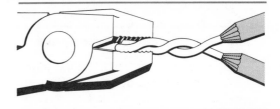

Figure 8.4   Twist with pliers

4. Cut the splice to about 2 cm in length, if necessary, as in Figure 8.5.

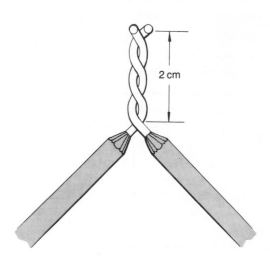

Figure 8.5   Completed rat-tail splice

Tee or Tap Splice

The tee or tap splice is used when a connection or joint is to be made on a conductor without cutting the conductor. The following is a step procedure for making a tee or tap splice:
1. Remove about 2.5 cm of the insulation from the conductor to be tapped (Figure 8.6).

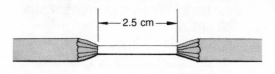

Figure 8.6   Conductor to be tapped

2. Remove about 5 cm of the insulation from the tapping conductor (Figure 8.7).

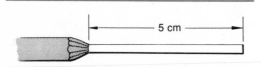

Figure 8.7   Tapping conductor

3. Place the conductors as in Figure 8.8 and with a pair of pliers hold the two conductors in this position.

Figure 8.8   Conductors in place

4. With the free hand, wrap the tapping conductor around the conductor about 4 or 5 turns (Figures 8.9 and 8.10).

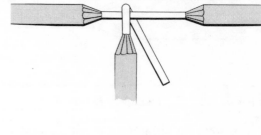

Figure 8.9   First turn

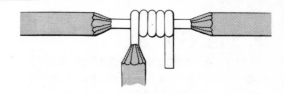

Figure 8.10   Five turns

5. Tighten the completed splice with a pair of pliers and remove any excess tapping conductor (Figure 8.11).

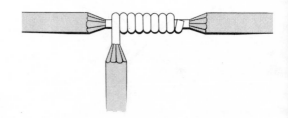

Figure 8.11   Completed tap splice

Introductory Electricity

Western Union Splice

The Western Union splice is used when the length of wire is to be extended or lengthened. This splice was named after the Western Union Telegraph Company years ago when they used this splice for the extension of their lines. The following is a step procedure for making a Western Union splice:

1. Remove about 7.5 cm of insulation from each conductor (Figure 8.12).

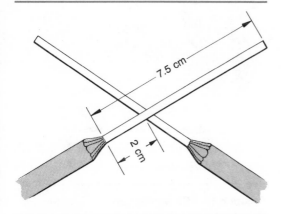

Figure 8.12   Conductors in place

2. Cross the conductors about 2 cm from the insulation (Figure 8.13).

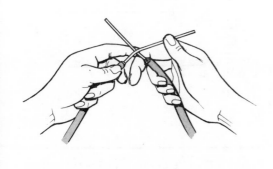

Figure 8.13   Cross conductors with free hand

3. Hold the wires firmly at the cross-over with a pair of pliers.
4. With the free hand, wrap one conductor in a clockwise direction about 4 or 5 turns (Figure 8.14).

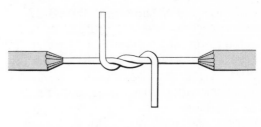

Figure 8.14   Conductor wrapped in one direction

5. Now wrap the free conductor in a counter-clockwise direction about 4 or 5 turns.
6. Complete the splice as shown in Figure 8.15 making sure the turns are tight around the other conductors.

Figure 8.15   Completed Western Union splice

7. Cut off any excess conductor and bend the ends down to prevent them from penetrating the insulation.

Soldering

The purpose of soldering a splice is to improve the mechanical strength of the splice and to prevent corrosion, which would reduce the conductivity of the splice. *Soldering will not improve a poor splice.*

Soft Soldering

Soft solder (half and half) is composed of 50% tin and 50% lead. 50/50 solder as it is called has a melting point of 212°C and is a general purpose solder. Other solders used are the 60/40 with a melting point of 188°C and the 63/37 compositions. The first figure of the ratio is the percentage of tin. For example, 60/40 means 60% tin and 40% lead. 60/40 solder may be used for radio and television work while 63/37 solder may be used for commutator soldering on motors and generators. Solder for electrical work is made in the forms of bar, ribbon, and wire. The wire form solder is used more than the others and sometimes has a flux in its core which makes it very convenient for small jobs.

Soldering Flux

To produce a smooth, evenly soldered joint, a suitable flux must be used. Rosin flux is best for electrical work because it prevents corrosion. Sal ammoniac is also suitable as it is a natural flux for copper.
NOTE: Never use a zinc chloride solution because it causes corrosion.

Great care must be exercised in flux application. Insufficient flux will permit oxygen to come in contact with the heated metal thereby forming oxide on its surface. If too much paste is used on delicate electrical apparatus it will spread over the surrounding surface, collect dust, cause corrosion, and conduct electricity. If too much rosin is used it may run over the surfaces of contacts and prevent the proper operation of the apparatus. The nature of the solder often determines the type of flux to be used.

Heat Application

The application of heat for most soldering jobs in electrical work is accomplished by the following four methods:
1. The electrical soldering gun and tips (Figures 8.16 and 8.17)

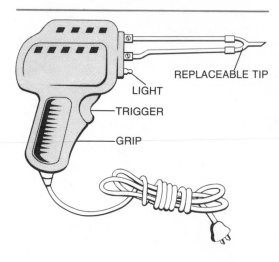

REPLACEABLE TIP
LIGHT
TRIGGER
GRIP

Figure 8.16   Soldering gun

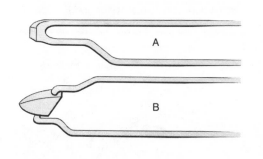

A

B

Figure 8.17   Soldering gun tips (A) cutting tip (B) smoothing tip

2. The electrical soldering copper and supports (Figures 8.18 and 8.19)

Introductory Electricity

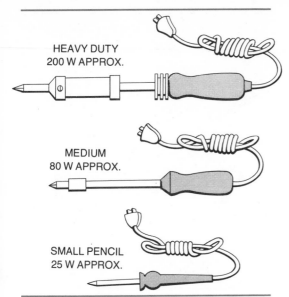

HEAVY DUTY
200 W APPROX.

MEDIUM
80 W APPROX.

SMALL PENCIL
25 W APPROX.

Figure 8.18   Electrical soldering coppers

Figure 8.19   Soldering-copper supports

3. The propane torch (Figure 8.20)

Figure 8.20   Propane torch

4. The blow torch (Figure 8.21)

Figure 8.21   Blow torch

Each of the above methods has its own specific use. For instance, soldering gun and soldering copper are used where the conductors are small and not too much heat is required for a great length of time. They are ideal for radio and television work. When just a few splices are to be soldered and a great amount of heat is required, the propane torch will be best suited for the job. However, when large numbers of splices have to be soldered and the conductors are large in diameter, the blow torch will serve best because of its greater heat. Blow torches for electrical work are being replaced by larger and more efficient propane or acetylene torches.

In any case, the choice of the application of heat to be used depends on (a) the amount of work to be done, (b) the type of work, (c) the most economical method.

Care in the Use of Torches

Extreme care must be taken when using propane torches and blow torches because they increase the danger of fire and explosion. When not in use, they should be stored in a metal cabinet to prevent any escaping gases that may cause a fire or explosion. Also, torches should not be used in a confined area due to the hazards of fire and gas fumes.

Tinning a Soldering Copper

The following is a step procedure for tinning the soldering copper:

1. File the four sides of the copper point until they are bright and smooth (Figure 8.22).

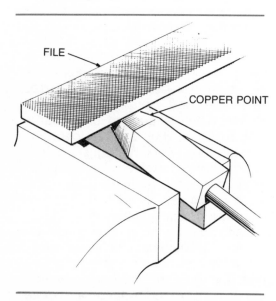

Figure 8.22   Filing the point

2. Heat the copper with a torch until it is hot enough to melt 50/50 solder freely.
3. Remove the copper from the heat and rub each side across a cake of sal ammoniac or soldering paste. This will clean the copper (Figure 8.23).

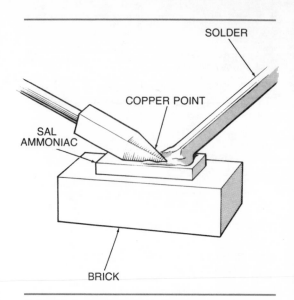

Figure 8.23   Tinning with sal ammoniac

4. Add a little solder to the copper while rubbing each side on the sal ammoniac or soldering paste until the copper is tinned. *Tinned* means that the solder has adhered to the copper.

NOTE: The soldering copper should not get red hot because this will burn the tinning and oxidize the copper which will require that the copper be retinned.

Figure 8.24 shows tinning a copper with rosin-core solder.

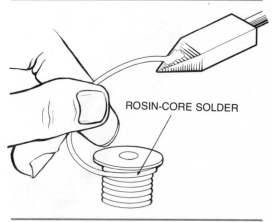

Figure 8.24   Tinning the soldering copper with rosin-core solder

Soldering with a Soldering Copper

The position of the tinned copper is important when soldering. Since heat tends to rise, the copper should be applied below the splice. Then, if a good contact is established between the soldering copper and the metal, the metal will conduct the heat in all directions. The solder on the copper makes contact with the splice and carries the heat into the metal. Care should be exercised in selecting a soldering copper of suitable size and shape. The face of the joint should rest on the tip of the copper to conduct as much heat as possible. The metal being soldered must be hotter than the melting point of the solder being applied or it will quickly form into a cooled, pasty mass. On fine work flux may be applied to the work with the point of a toothpick and enough molten solder conveyed to the joint by the tip of the copper. Rosin-core solder provides solder and flux in proper proportion for direct application to the joint, but more heat is required when using rosin as a flux and all oxide must first be removed from the joint.

Soldering with an Electric Soldering Copper

The following step procedure describes the method for soldering a splice (Figure 8.25):

1. Plug the soldering copper into an electrical outlet and set it on the soldering stand.
2. Place a small amount of soldering flux (paste) all over the splice.
3. Test the soldering copper from time to time with a piece of wire solder (50/50). The copper should be hot enough to melt the solder quickly.

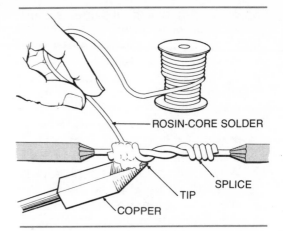

Figure 8.25   **Soldering a splice**

4. When the copper is hot enough, place the tip under the splice, as shown in Figure 8.25, until the paste has melted and run down through all parts of the splice.
5. Touch the end of the wire solder to the splice until it melts and runs down through all parts of the splice.
6. Shake or wipe the excess solder from the splice. It is not necessary or desirable to fill all the cracks or holes in the splice. If enough heat is used, the excess solder will run out.

For Review

1. Why must wires never be skinned with the knife held at right angles to the wire?
2. Where would a rat-tail splice be used?
3. Where are tee splices used?
4. When are Western Union splices used? How did the splice get its name?
5. State the purpose of soldering.
6. Why must all electrical splices be both electrically and mechanically secure before they are soldered?
7. What composition of solder should be used for soldering electrical joints and splices?

8. What composition of solder is used for radio work? Why?

9. Under what conditions need a splice not be soldered?

10. What types of flux must be avoided when soldering electrical connections? Why?

11. Name four methods by which heat may be applied for soldering electrical work.

12. Why is it important to apply proper heat to a splice when soldering?

13. Why is the soldering copper held on the underside of conductors that are to be soldered?

14. What is the purpose of the soldering iron support?

15. What type of heat application would be most suitable when a large amount of soldering must be done?

16. What is meant by tinning?

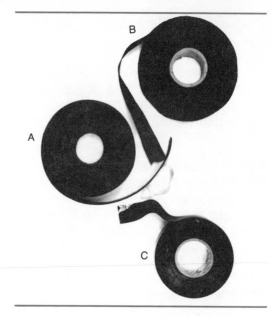

Figure 8.26   (A) Vinyl thermoplastic tape (B) Friction tape (C) Rubber tape

Electrical Insulating Tapes

Electrical manufacturers produce three different insulating tapes:
(1) Vinyl thermoplastic (Figure 8.26A)
    (i) may be used alone
    (ii) is the equivalent of any insulation removed from conductors for 600 V or less
(2) Cotton tape or friction tape (Figure 8.26B)
    (i) may be used alone only on circuits of extra low voltage (30 V or less)
    (ii) is used to protect rubber tape from injury on higher voltage circuits
(3) Splicing compound or rubber tape (Figure 8.26C)
    (i) is seldom used alone
    (ii) is generally applied to splice first and then covered over with friction tape for protection

The Power Commission Act for Ontario (Hydro Code) states that the insulation that is replaced on a splice must be equivalent to the amount that was removed. An equivalent to rubber and friction tape could be approved plastic tape.

When plastic tape is used, care must be taken that sufficient tape be applied to prevent any sharp projections from piercing the insulation. In any case, the amount of insulation replaced on the splice must insure adequate protection against short circuits and electrical shock.

NOTE: All joints and splices must have a coating of insulating varnish to prevent the insulation from drying out.

The following is a step procedure (Figures 8.27 to 8.31) for insulating a splice using rubber tape and friction tape:
1. Be sure the splice is free from any sharp projections which might puncture the tape.
2. Wrap the splice carefully with rubber tape, pulling hard on the tape to stretch it to about half of its original

width. This is necessary to ensure an air-tight and moisture-proof joint. Make sure that the rubber tape covers the splice from one end of the insulation to the other end.

Figure 8.27   Solder fills space between turns of wire

Figure 8.28   Rubber tape is wrapped on joint

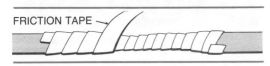

Figure 8.29   Friction tape is wound on rubber tape

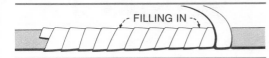

Figure 8.30   Filling in and winding in half-lap fashion

Figure 8.31   Completed joint

Figure 8.32 shows a cross-section of a completed Western Union splice.

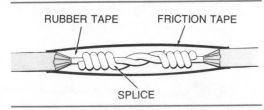

Figure 8.32   Cross-section of completed Western Union splice

3. Starting at the other end of the finished rubber tape, wrap the splice with friction tape pulling hard to produce a neat job. Make sure that the friction tape covers the splice from the insulation at one end to the insulation at the other end. The thickness of the finished insulation should be slightly larger than the thickness of the original insulation of the wire. Figure 8.33 shows a step procedure for taping a rat-tail splice.

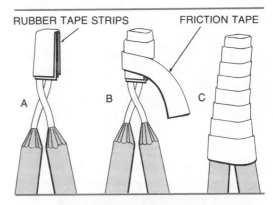

Figure 8.33   Steps in taping a rat-tail splice: (A) laying strips of rubber tape on a rat-tail joint (B) winding friction tape on splice (C) finished joint

Solderless Wire Connectors

Various types of solderless wire connectors have been developed and approved for making connections in electrical wiring when there is no mechanical strain on the joint. They eliminate the need for soldering and are made of an insulating material so that connections need not be taped. When they are installed correctly, short circuits and faulty open circuits cannot occur. Time and labour can be saved by their use.

There are two common types of solderless wire connectors available. One type has a threaded metal spring molded into the plastic body (Figure 8.34). The other type has a removable brass fitting supplied with a set-screw for securing the wires (Figure 8.35). Set-screws may have a standard slot head or the newer socket head. The insulating shell screws over the brass fitting.

The following procedure will show how to install a wire connector.

To Install a Twist-on Wire Connector (Figure 8.34)

1. Remove approximately 1.5 cm of insulation from two #14 conductors. Scrape clean.
2. Hold the two conductor ends even and insert the ends into the connector shell.
3. Twist the connector clockwise onto the wires until it is tight. Be certain that no bare wire is visible.
4. Test the connection by trying to pull the connector away from the wires.

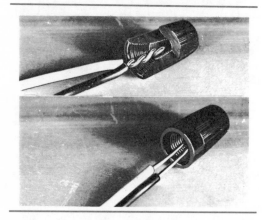

Figure 8.34   Solderless twist-on connector

To Install a Set-Screw Connector (Figure 8.35)

1. Remove approximately 1.5 cm of insulation from two #14 conductors. Scrape clean.
2. Remove the brass fitting from its shell and loosen the set screw.

3. Place the brass fitting over the ends of the wires so that the threaded shoulder is next to the insulation.
4. Tighten the set screw to make a good electrical connection.
5. Cut off any excess wire that extends beyond the brass fitting.
6. Thread the bakelite shell onto the brass fitting until snug.
7. Be certain that no bare wire is visible and that there is no possibility of the shell unscrewing accidentally.
8. Test the connection by trying to pull the connector away from the wires.

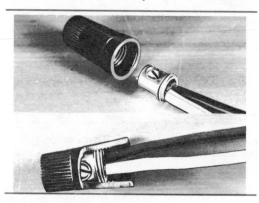

Figure 8.35   Set-screw connector

Terminal Eyes

Most electrical connections which are made to equipment use terminal screws. Exercise proper precautions when making these connections to ensure proper operation of the equipment and to prevent trouble during operation. Consideration must, however, be given to the type of insulation that covers the conductor. The following is a step procedure for making terminal eyes and connecting them to terminal screws.

Solid Conductors

1. Remove about 2 cm of insulation. (Clean wire thoroughly.)
2. Bend the bare connector 90 degrees (Figure 8.36).

Introductory Electricity

Figure 8.36

3. Using pliers, make a loop in the end of the conductor (Figure 8.37).

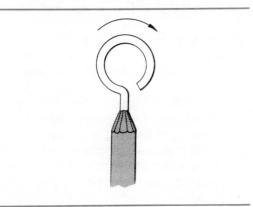

Figure 8.37

4. Bend this end of the conductor (Figure 8.38).

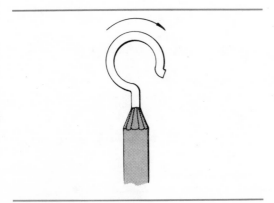

Figure 8.38

5. Place this loop under the terminal screw in the direction in which the screw tightens.
6. Squeeze the eye loop closed and tighten the terminal screw (Figure 8.39).

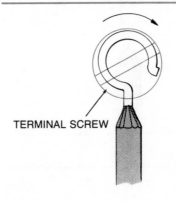

TERMINAL SCREW

Figure 8.39

NOTE: Make certain that the loop goes under and around the terminal screw in the direction in which it tightens.

NOTE: Terminal screws on electrical equipment are not intended to be completely removed. Therefore, do not apply too much force.

Stranded Conductors

To prevent stranded conductors from unwinding and causing short circuits and grounds, the ends are specially prepared before they are connected to terminals as follows:

1. Remove 2 cm of insulation from the end (Figure 8.40).
2. Twist the strands with pliers (Figure 8.41).
3. Solder the strands.
4. Form an eye loop (Figure 8.42).
5. Cut off the excess wire.
6. Place the loop in the direction in which the screw tightens (Figure 8.42).

Figure 8.40

Figure 8.41

Figure 8.42

For Review

1. How much insulation must be replaced on bare splices?
2. What purpose is served by the rubber tape?
3. Is friction tape classified as a good insulator?
4. Could a splice be insulated with friction tape alone? Explain.
5. What are the two main advantages in using vinyl thermoplastic tape?
6. Name two types of solderless connectors.
7. State the purpose of a solderless connector.
8. Name two advantages and two disadvantages of solderless connectors.
9. What is meant by the term "solid conductor"?
10. Where are stranded conductors used?
11. Why are stranded conductors soldered before they are wrapped around screws or terminals?
12. What possible danger is present when stranded conductors are not properly prepared before they are fastened to the terminals?
13. Which way are eye loops wrapped around the terminals? Why?

9

Electrical Symbols for Signal Wiring

In every trade there are signs or symbols used to designate certain articles or equipment used by that trade. The

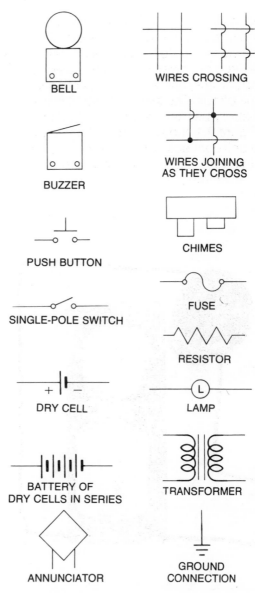

BELL

WIRES CROSSING

BUZZER

WIRES JOINING AS THEY CROSS

PUSH BUTTON

CHIMES

SINGLE-POLE SWITCH

FUSE

RESISTOR

DRY CELL

LAMP

BATTERY OF DRY CELLS IN SERIES

TRANSFORMER

ANNUNCIATOR

GROUND CONNECTION

Signal Circuits, Devices, and Wiring

electrical trade has its symbols, a language all its own. Symbols save time and space on blueprints and drawings. These "short forms" are universal and are usually drawn to scale. They should be learned thoroughly so they may be recognized immediately.

Bell Circuit Components

Most, if not all, electrical installations include some type of signal circuit. All electrical signal circuits contain a source of power, some type of signal apparatus, and a means of activating the circuit. The simplest circuit is the battery bell set used by electricians. Figure 9.1 shows a one cell battery and a bell connected in series with a pair of test wires. Figure 9.2 shows the schematic circuit for the one cell battery test set.

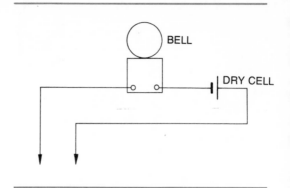

Figure 9.2   Battery bell test set

The set is checked by touching together the ends of the lead wires. If the bell sounds, it is ready for use in testing. It is used to ring out conductors for continuity, short circuits, and grounds. By connecting the two open leads to a push button, we have a simple signal circuit. Figure 9.3 shows such a simple circuit.

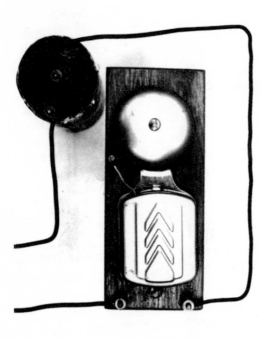

Figure 9.1   One cell battery and bell test set

Figure 9.3   Simple circuit

Introductory Electricity

Figure 9.4 shows the schematic for a simple circuit.

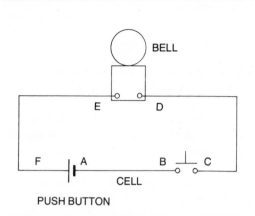

Figure 9.4   Simple circuit

The basic parts or sections of a complete simple circuit are as follows:
Point A to B: feeder section
Point C to D: control section
Point E to F: return section

Source of Power

In modern installations the primary cell has been replaced by the bell ringing transformer. It is used on alternating current lighting circuits to reduce the 120 V to a value of 6 to 10 V. This is the voltage required to activate buzzers and bells. Figure 9.5 shows a typical bell transformer.

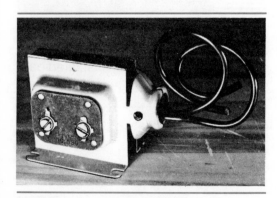

Figure 9.5   Bell transformer

Bell Transformers

Bell transformers are also made for a secondary voltage of 12 to 18 V for operating door chimes. Bell transformers are designed and constructed so as to operate continuously on the lighting circuit. If the signal circuit becomes short circuited, the current will be limited to the rating of the transformer.

Electric Bell and Buzzer

The bell and buzzer are examples of the application of electromagnets. Figure 9.6 shows the construction of a bell. A buzzer is similar but lacks the hammer (or gong) and bell.

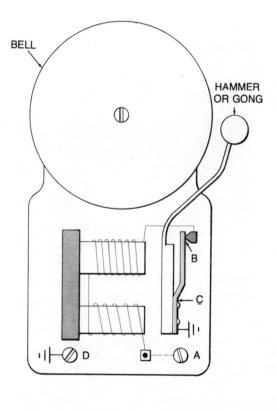

Figure 9.6   Vibrating bell

Signal Circuits, Devices and Wiring

Two small coils are mounted on iron cores to form the electromagnet. Current passes from terminal A through the coils, contact B and the armature C, to the frame, and to terminal D, completing the circuit.

The current energizes the electromagnets which attract the armature. This opens the contacts and causes the current to stop. The electromagnets then lose their magnetism and the armature spring closes the contacts. If the electric power is left on terminals A and D, the operation is repeated and it will continue until the power is interrupted. Each operation causes the hammer to strike the bell, and since the operations occur rapidly the armature, contact spring, and hammer vibrate rapidly.

Push Button

A push button is a device used to open and close a low voltage circuit. An insulated button extending through a cover is used to press a spring to close the circuit. When the button is released the spring opens the circuit. Figure 9.7 illustrates a typical push button and Figure 9.8 shows the internal section of the push button.

Bell Conductors

Bell conductors consist of copper wire covered with two layers of cotton wrapped in opposite directions. Both layers of the cotton are impregnated with paraffin. Conductors can also be covered with synthetic insulating materials, such as plastic.

The usual size of bell wire is #18 gauge since the current for such circuits is limited. Two or three bell conductors are often twisted together and covered with a protective overall sheath to form a cable. Each wire in the cable has a different colour marking for identification purposes. Bell wiring is fastened to surfaces with insulated staples. Figure 9.9 illustrates three types of annunciator wire.

Figure 9.7   Push button

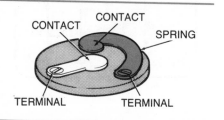

Figure 9.8   Push button—internal view

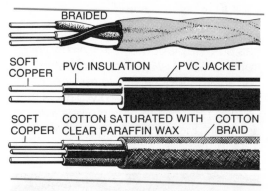

Figure 9.9   Annunciator wires

Figure 9.10 shows an insulated bell wire staple.

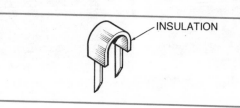

Figure 9.10   Insulated staple

Ontario Hydro regulations state that bell wiring shall not be placed in any raceway, compartment, outlet, junction box, or similar fitting with light and power circuits unless the conductors of the two circuits are separated by a suitable barrier. It also states that open conductors shall be separated by at least 5 cm from light or power conductors which are not contained in a raceway or encased in approved, non-metallic, flexible tubing or in porcelain tubes or an equivalent device.

Typical Signal Circuits

The electrician must be in possession of certain information before he can make plans to connect any electrical circuit. The principal items of information include:

1. voltage of the supply circuit
2. capacity of the apparatus to be operated
3. location of the apparatus with respect to location of the supply

Figure 9.11 shows a simple bell circuit connected from a 120 to a 6 V transformer, through a push button, to a 6 V bell. The transformer is used on alternating current supply. If alternating current is not available, a 6 V battery would operate the bell.

Parallel-Connected Push Buttons

Shown in Figure 9.12 is one additional push button station with connections for the operation of the bell from two independent locations.

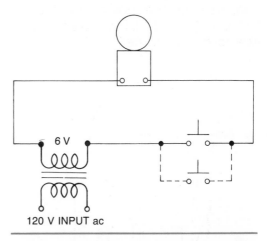

Figure 9.12   Parallel-connected push buttons

Figure 9.11   Simple bell circuit connected to a 6 V transformer

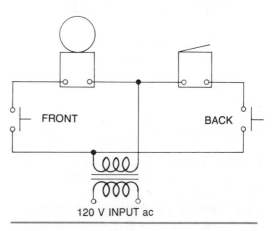

Figure 9.13   Front-and-back-door system

Front-and-Back-Door Systems

Figure 9.13 shows a schematic for the ordinary signal circuit used in many homes. A buzzer is used for the signal from one door, while the bell is used for the signal from the other door. The transformer is shown in symbol form.

Buzzabell

A combination unit with the bell and buzzer in the same case has been developed to replace separate bells and buzzers. Figure 9.14 illustrates this device called a buzzabell.

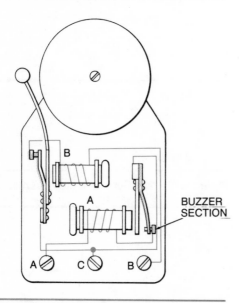

Figure 9.14　　**Buzzabell**

Operation of the Buzzabell

Current enters at A, passes through the coil A, to the circuit breaker of the buzzer, through the armature, and returns by C. This activates the buzzer section. When current enters at B, it goes through coil B, circuit breaker, armature, and re-

turns by C. This activates the bell. Each part of the buzzabell is controlled by separate push buttons.

For Review

1. Name the sections of a simple bell circuit.
2. What device has replaced the dry cell in bell and buzzer systems?
3. Why is this device more advantageous than dry cells?
4. How much voltage is required to energize a bell or buzzer?
5. What causes the armature in a bell to vibrate?
6. If one coil is short-circuited, will the bell operate on the other coil?
7. State the action of the circuit breaker in a bell.
8. Why is soft iron used as the core of the electromagnet?
9. What is the purpose of a push button?
10. What type and size of wire are used for signal systems?
11. How is the wiring secured in signal systems?
12. State the two Ontario Hydro regulations which cover signal wiring.
13. What is a buzzabell?
14. State the buzzabell's advantages over bells and buzzers.

Series-Connected Devices (Loads)

Vibrating bells may also be connected in series, as shown in Figure 9.15.

There is a disadvantage in series bell circuits because if there is an "open" in any part of the circuit, all devices cease to operate. Also, more voltage is required to operate the device. Figure 9.16 shows the schematic of series-connected bells.

Introductory Electricity

Figure 9.15   Series-connected bells

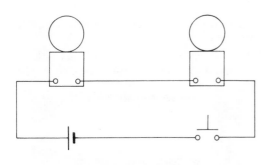

Figure 9.16   Series-connected bells

Figure 9.17   Parallel-connected bells

Parallel-Connected Devices (Loads)

Bells, buzzers and most devices are usually connected in parallel (Figure 9.17).

This type of circuit allows devices in different locations to operate at the same time. This circuit is typical of the bell system in schools and the lighting system in our homes. Figure 9.18 shows the schematic for parallel-connected bells.

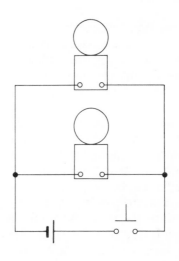

Figure 9.18   Parallel-connected bells

Door Chimes

The door chime is replacing the bell-and-buzzer system. A typical door chime is shown in Figure 9.19. The wiring is the same as for the bell-and-buzzer system. Some of the more elaborate types of chimes may have several tones and require extra wiring. The internal connections for another type of chime are shown in Figure 9.20.

Figure 9.19   Door chime

Operation of the Door Chime

When the front-door push button is pressed, current enters through coil A and returns through the transformer terminal T. Coil A is energized and draws the core into the coil with enough force to strike the bottom tone bar. This puts the spring under tension. When coil A is de-energized, the core springs back and strikes the top tone bar; thus two tones are chimed (Figure 9.20).

When the back-door push button is pressed, current enters through coil B and returns through the transformer terminal T. Coil B is energized and draws the core into the coil with enough force to strike the bottom tone bar. This puts the spring under tension. When coil B is de-energized, the core springs back and strikes the top tone bar. There

is no sound because the top of the core is padded; therefore only one tone is chimed.

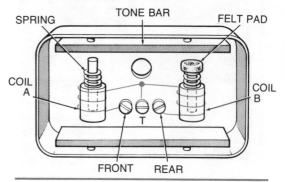

Figure 9.20   Internal connection of a door chime

Annunciators

To receive signals from a number of push buttons located at different points throughout a building a device called an *annunciator* is used. Figure 9.21 illustrates a 4-point gravity-drop annunciator.

Figure 9.21   4-point gravity-drop annunciator

Operation of the Annunciator

Behind each number there is an electromagnet that holds up a number. When the current energizes this magnet it causes an indicating device to drop, allowing the number to be shown. At the same time a bell or buzzer is energized so that attention is called to the device. An annunciator has to be reset after operation by a reset button. Some annunciators have automatic resets and lamps may be used instead of bells or buzzers.

Annunciators are used in elevators, offices, hospitals, factories, sprinkler systems, fire halls, hotels, and schools. Figure 9.22 shows the internal wiring of a 4-point gravity-drop annunciator.

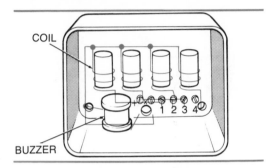

Figure 9.22   Internal connections of a 4-point annunciator

Operation of the Gravity Number Drop

When current flows in the coil, the core becomes an electromagnet (Figure 9.23). The magnet will attract the armature which is pivoted at A. Resting on the armature claw and pivoted at B is a shutter with a number on it. This shutter drops, showing the number. After the electromagnet is de-energized, the armature returns to its original position. The number can now be reset manually.

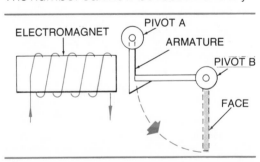

Figure 9.23   Operation of the gravity number drop

Installation of Annunciators

Since the gravity-drop annunciator is dependent upon the number dropping due to gravity, it must be mounted straight and on a flat vertical surface. In this position the number drops are free to fall when the electromagnets are energized.

The operating voltage is supplied from a transformer, a series of dry cells, or a battery. Ten volts are necessary to operate the annunciator because the bell or buzzer is connected in series with the coils that operate the drops.

Wiring for signal systems is usually either single conductor annunciator wire or an insulated type cable containing two or more identified conductors. The wire is secured with insulated electrician staples.

Electrical Terms Used in Circuitry

Live or Alive: This means that a conductor is connected to a source of supply and there is danger of electric shock.
Dead: This means that a conductor is not connected to a source of supply and there is no danger of electric shock.
Open Circuit: This means the circuit is broken and no current is flowing, but some parts or devices in the circuit may be live and there may be danger of electric shock.
Closed circuit: This means the current is flowing in a conductor, that the conductors are live, and that the circuit is completed through a device.
Short Circuit: This means that the circuit resistance has been reduced to *zero* and therefore a very large current flows. This occurs when a live conductor touches ground or when two live wires touch each other.

For Review

1. What device is fast replacing the bell-and-buzzer system?
2. State the advantages of this system.
3. What is an annunciator?
4. Name five places where annunciators may be used.
5. Why is the annunciator reset?
6. Where are the automatic resets used?
7. With the aid of a diagram, describe the operation of the gravity drop.
8. Define (a) an open circuit, (b) a short circuit, (c) a live circuit.
9. What precautions must be observed when installing annunciators? Why?
10. How much voltage is required to operate an annunciator? Why?

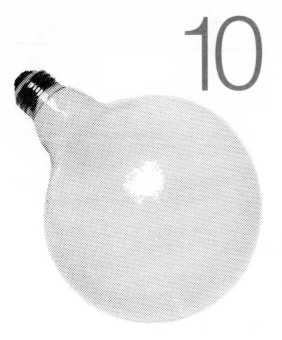

10

Electrical energy is measured by the watt hour meter. This is the familiar type of meter (Figure 10.1) used in the home to determine the amount of power consumption in calculating the electric bill. The dial is shown in Figure 10.2.

Courtesy Sangamo Company Limited

Figure 10.1   Kilowatt hour meter

The energy used by electrical devices is the rate at which energy is being used (power) multiplied by the time that the devices are in use. When power is measured in watts and the time in hours, then

POWER x TIME = ENERGY
WATTS x HOURS = WATT HOURS

The watt hour is a relatively small unit. A kilowatt (kW) equals 1000 W; therefore the kilowatt hour equals 1000 W·h. Two readings are necessary for a monthly or quarterly calculation. The meter does not return to zero after a reading is taken, it keeps on registering. To find how much electricity was used in a given period, it is necessary to know the readings of the meter at the beginning and end of the period and to subtract one from the other. The dials are read from left to right.

The
Watt Hour
Meter

To Read a Watt Hour Meter

1. To read the March reading, Figure 10.2, begin at the left dial marked 10 000. This means that a full revolution of the pointer stands for 10 000 kW·h. Write the number that the pointer has passed; in this case the number is 3.

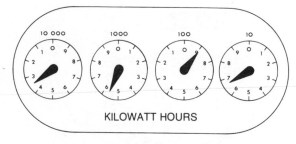

Figure 10.2   March dial reading

2. Read the next dial to the right. This reads 5.
3. Read the next dial to the right. This reads 8.
4. Read the next dial to the right. This reads 7. This dial is always read at the closest number to the pointer. The full reading is 3587 kW·h.

NOTE: The pointers on adjacent dials revolve in opposite directions. If in doubt as to whether the pointer has just passed a figure or is just arriving at it, refer to the previous figure to the right. If it is 0 or 1 the figure in question has been passed. If it is 8 or 9 the figure has not been passed. The figure passed is always used.

We pay for electricity by the number of kilowatt hours we have consumed. Some industrial plants pay a flat rate for their power. For example, a factory consumes 1800 kW·h in one month. The rate is 3¢/kW·h. Calculate the power bill for the plant.

Since the rate for power is 3¢/kW·h and the power consumed is 1800 kW·h, the cost to the plant is 3 x 1800 = $54.00

Calculating a Residential Power Bill

Although the domestic consumer also pays for power by the number of kilowatt hours consumed, there is no flat rate. Instead there are several rates and a discount is given for payment before a specified due date.

A typical household bill would be calculated as follows:
Present meter reading: 6710
Previous meter reading: 5930
Amount consumed: 780

Residential Rates Bi-monthly (Net)
First 100 kW·h . . . . . 4.4¢
Next 400 kW·h . . . . . 2.2¢
Additional kW·h . . . . . 1.08¢
First 100 kW·h cost 1.00 x 4.4   = $ 4.40
Next 400 kW·h cost 400 x 2.2   =   8.80
Balance kW·h is
    780 − 500 = 280 x 1.08   =   3.02
Total cost or gross   = 16.22
Discount at 10% for payment
    before due date   =   1.62
Net   =$14.60

For Review

1. How is electrical energy measured?
2. How many watts are in a kilowatt?

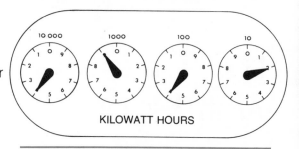

Figure 10.3   June dial reading

3. What is the June reading in Figure 10.3?
4. What amount of electrical energy was used from March to June?
5. How do you decide if the pointer has just arrived at or has just passed a figure?
6. Which dial of a watt hour meter is read first?
7. How many kilowatt hours are used if a March reading is 9962 and a June reading is 0185?
8. Write the readings shown on the meters of Figure 10.4.

NO. 1

NO. 2

NO. 3

NO. 4

Figure 10.4

9. If the reading of #2 was taken on April 30th, and reading #1 was taken on June 30th, what is the power bill for the two months if power is 4¢/kW·h?

10. If the reading of #4 was taken on January 2nd and reading of #3 was taken on March 1st, what is the power bill for the two months if power costs 3.4¢/kW·h

11. Calculate the power bill if the reading of #4 was taken in August and the reading of #2 in October. Power is at a cost of 4.5¢/kW·h.

12. The power rates on certain power bills are as follows:
First 50 kW·h: 3.5¢
Next 400 kW·h: 1.5¢
Balance kW·h: 0.8¢
Allowing for a 10% discount on each bill, calculate the following:
(a) present reading 3465 previous 1342
(b) present reading 5100 previous 3465
(c) present reading 7590 previous 5100
(d) present reading 8001 previous 7590

13. Bring in a paid power bill. Calculate the power costs and check it with the Hydro's calculations and costs.

14. (a) Make a table with headings in the order given: Name of appliance; Rating in watts; Time operated (approximately) per week; Kilowatt hours cost (at 4¢/kW·h).

(b) In this table list the electrical appliances in your home (no lamps) and insert the above information.

Name of appliance	Rating in watts	Time operated per week	kW·h cost at 5¢/kW·h

15. Make a table, as in question 14, for the lights with the following headings: Name of room; Number of lights; Wattage; Time operated approximately; Kilowatt hours cost (at 2c/kW·h).

Name of room	No. of lamps	Wattage	Time operated per week	kW·h cost at 5¢/kW·h

16. Which type of appliance requires the greatest amount of power?

17. Compare the power cost with the light cost and determine the percentage.

Introductory Electricity

Electric Cords and Attachments

11

Portable Electric Cords

Electrical cords may be placed in four classes:
1. Lamp cords
2. Appliance cords
3. Lamp extension cords
4. Power extension cords

Lamp Cords. This electrical cord is generally made from two-wire parallel cords (Figure 11.1). It has a two-prong attachment plug on one end and a lamp socket on the other. This cord should only be used for portable lights, such as bed lights, table lights, and other similar lamps. Lamp cord should never be used for portable electrical tools, such as electric drills, and it should never be stapled to baseboards for extensions around a room. Code letters for this cord are SPT1 and SPT2, depending upon the thickness of the insulation.

Figure 11.1   SPT parallel cords

Appliance Cords. All portable electrical heating appliances are equipped with a special cord that has insulation which will resist the heat that is conducted back from the appliance along the copper conductor. This cord generally has two conductors, each with a rubber insulation and enclosed with a heavy layer of asbestos. This is wrapped with a strong layer of cotton (Figure 11.2). A two-prong attachment plug is connected to one end and a special appliance body is connected to the other end for connection to the electrical appliance. This cord is coded HPD.

Some heating appliances have a new type of heater cord that is connected directly to the appliance. This cord has the appearance of the twin

Figure 11.2   HPD Asbestos heater cord

lamp cord but has a heavier insulation of rubber and asbestos. Code letters are HPN. Figure 11.3 shows the HPN cord.

Figure 11.3   HPN heater cord

Lamp Extension Cords.   Portable lamp extension cords are constructed of three individual conductors each with a rubber insulation of a different colour: one green, one white, and one black. The three conductors are covered with a heavy layer of black rubber. This cord is coded SJ cable (Figure 11.4).

Figure 11.4   SJ extension cord

A three-prong U-ground attachment plug is installed on one end and a weatherproof lampholder on the other end. The plug has the green wire connected to the U-ground terminal, the black wire connected to the bronze terminal, and the white wire connected to the silver terminal. The lampholder is connected by joining the white wire of the cord to the white wire of the lamp socket and the black wire is joined to the black wire. The green wire is connected

to the wire lamp guard that is placed over the lamp for protection.

Power Extension Cords.   The same type of cable is used for this cord as for the lamp extension cord. A three-prong U-ground attachment plug is connected to one end and a three-wire U-ground attachment body is installed on the other end with the same colours of wire connected to the terminals as on the plug. This type of cord, SJ cable, is used on portable electric tools, such as drills, sanders, and saws.

Figure 11.5   Two-prong plug cap

Figure 11.6   U-ground plug cap

Electrical Devices

Plug Caps.   There are two main types of attachment plug caps. One is the standard *two-prong parallel plug cap* shown in Figure 11.5 and the other is the *U-ground or polarized plug cap* shown in Figure 11.6.

The two-prong plug cap is the most familiar one in your home. It may be made of bakelite, rubber, or plastic and has different shapes, but usually it has two brass prongs to receive the current. They are used on lamps, radios, toasters, and irons.

The other main type of plug cap (the U-ground or polarized plug cap) is

Introductory Electricity

heavier in construction, is usually made of rubber, and has three prongs. Two of the prongs are parallel, one coloured silver and the other brass. The third prong is brass in colour and has a U shape. The terminal which is connected to this prong is coloured green and is called the grounding terminal. This type of plug cap is called a polarized plug because the prongs are always inserted in the same position. They are used on heavy portable equipment, such as washers and dryers, portable tools, and where there is unusual danger from electric shock, such as basements and damp places.

Appliance Plugs. The connection of heating appliances is made with a type of plug attachment known as the appliance plug (Figure 11.7).

It is a rugged device and is constructed of a two piece bakelite cover fastened together with nuts and bolts. Connections to the prongs are made with an asbestos-covered cord called a heater cord, HPD, because it can withstand the heat from the appliance.

Figure 11.7   Appliance plug

Appliance plugs are used on toasters, irons, heaters, tea kettles, electric grills, and other appliances that generate heat. They are not polarized and therefore require only two wires. The spring is used to prevent the cord from kinking at the plug. Appliance plugs may have built-in switches to discon-

nect the current, or be plain as shown in Figure 11.7.

Sockets.   Lamp sockets used with extension cords and lamps are of several types. Figures 11.8 and 11.9 show the push-through socket and the keyless socket. Others, not shown, are the key and the pull-chain sockets. The construction of each is practically the same: cap base, cardboard lining, and shell. Each type of socket has its own advantage. For example, the keyless socket requires a switch to operate it while others may be used on table lamps and wall fixtures. The screw in the top of the cap is to hold a conduit nipple tight, if the socket is to be used in a fixture. The cap and shell are usually made of brass or plated brass or are nickel plated.

Figure 11.8   Push-through socket

Figure 11.9   Keyless brass socket

To Make and Assemble an Attachment for an Extension Cord

NOTE: Since lamp cord is always made of stranded wire, care must be taken to prevent cutting these strands. If the strands are cut the current-carrying capacity of the cord is reduced, and this may cause overheating at the terminal screws.

Materials: One lamp socket, one two-prong plug cap, SPT lamp cord

Procedure:
1. Disassemble the socket into its individual parts (Figure 11.10).

Figure 11.10   Disassembled socket

2. Insert the SP cord through the cap.
3. Remove about 2 cm of insulation from the end of each wire. Solder the end of each wire.
4. Connect one end of each wire to a terminal on the base of the lamp socket. Be sure that the wire is wrapped around the terminal in the direction that the screw tightens.
5. Assemble. The shell should fit inside the base and snap into position.
6. To prevent the wires from being pulled out from the terminals, a small amount of tape may be put under the cap.

To Connect the Plug Cap

Procedure
1. Insert the other end of the cord through the plug cap.
2. Remove about 2 cm of the insulation from the end of each wire. Solder the end of each wire.
3. Wrap each end of the insulated part of the wire around each prong as shown in Figure 11.11.

Figure 11.11   Connection to a two-prong plug cap

4. Connect one end of each wire to a terminal screw (Figure 11.11). Make sure that the wire is wrapped around the terminal screw in the same direction that it tightens.
5. Tighten the screws. Pull the cord snugly.
NOTE: (1) Soldering the ends of the wire will prevent the wires from flaring out from under the screw terminal.
  (2) Do not tighten the screws too tightly or you might strip the thread.

To Connect a U-Ground Plug Cap

Procedure:
1. With three-wire cord follow the same procedure as for the two-prong plug cap.
2. Connect the green (ground) wire to the green terminal (Figure 11.12).

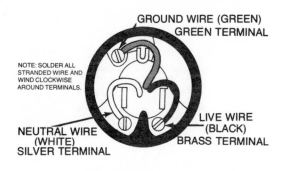

NOTE: SOLDER ALL STRANDED WIRE AND WIND CLOCKWISE AROUND TERMINALS.

GROUND WIRE (GREEN)
GREEN TERMINAL

LIVE WIRE (BLACK)
BRASS TERMINAL

NEUTRAL WIRE (WHITE)
SILVER TERMINAL

Figure 11.12   Connection to a U-ground plug cap

To Make an Appliance Plug

Materials: One appliance plug, asbestos cord, two-prong plug cap, glue

Procedure:

1. Take the appliance plug apart carefully and examine. Do not lose the small nuts and screws.
2. Slip the spring over the end of the cord.
3. Remove 3.75 cm of the outer covering and separate the two wires. Leave the asbestos on each wire.
4. Remove 2 cm of the rubber insulation from each wire. *Do not nick the wire.* Solder the ends of each wire.
5. Twist the asbestos around each wire and apply a small amount of glue so that the asbestos will not flare out.
6. Wrap a narrow band of friction tape at the end of the outer covering.
7. Make neat and connect one end of each wire to a terminal screw.
8. Fit the rubber cord into the grooves as shown in Figure 11.13.

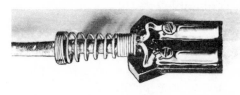

Figure 11.13   Appliance plug connection

9. Slip the spring into place.
10. Fit and secure the other half of the appliance plug with the nuts and screws.
11. Attach a two-prong plug cap at the other end of the cord.

NOTE: Neatness and mechanical security are of the utmost importance.

The purpose of leaving the asbestos around the rubber insulation is to prevent the rubber from being subjected to excess heat, which may make it crack and cause a short circuit.

Procedure: HPN Cord

1. Follow procedure 1 and 2 for asbestos wire.
2. Remove about 2 cm of rubber insulation from each wire. Do not nick the wire.
3. Solder the ends of each wire.
4. Connect the ends of each wire to a terminal screw.
5. Fit the HPN cord into the grooves as in Figure 11.13.
6. Assemble the appliance plug in the same manner as for the asbetos connection.
7. Attach a two-prong plug cap on the other end.

For Review

1. What are the two main types of plug caps?
2. Why is the rubber constructed type preferable?
3. What is the purpose of the U-grounding prong?
4. What is meant by polarized?
5. State two places where each plug cap is most suitable.
6. Where is the appliance plug used? Why?
7. What is heater cord?
8. State the purpose of the spring on the appliance plug.
9. Name four types of lamp sockets.
10. State two places where lamps sockets may be used.
11. What precaution should be taken when removing the insulation from stranded wire? Why?
12. Why is cord wire usually stranded?
13. How are wires connected around a terminal screw?
14. How can you prevent stranded wire from flaring out from beneath the terminal screw?
15. Why is the wire wrapped around the prong on a plug cap?

12

Screwdrivers

The screwdriver is the tool that installs or removes screws. It has, however, been erroneously substituted for many tools, varying from a crowbar to a pop bottle opener.

There are three main parts to a screwdriver: the *handle* is the part that you grasp when using it. The *shank* is the steel part that comes out of the handle and reaches to the blade. The *blade* is the shaped end that fits into the slots in screw heads (Figure 12.1). The length of a screwdriver includes the length of the blade and the portion of the shank not in the handle. The shank should *not* pass through the handle for electrical work. The handles are made of wood or plastic composition. Standard screwdrivers come in lengths from 6 cm to 45 cm.

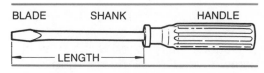

BLADE   SHANK   HANDLE
└── LENGTH ──┘

Figure 12.1   Screwdriver

The steel shank is made from alloy steel to withstand considerable twisting. It will, however, bend or crack if used as a lever and, once bent, it is difficult to straighten. If the shank is not straight, it is hard to keep the blade centred in the screw slots.

Types of Screwdrivers

The *standard blade* is shown in Figure 12.2 and is used for most ordinary work. The blades are shaped to meet requirements of the trade.

Figure 12.2   Standard blade

Hand Tools

The *small blade* screwdriver, Figure 12.3, is made with a narrow shank and is used in confined spaces where the blade of the standard screwdriver is too wide.

Figure 12.3   Small blade

The close quarters or *stubby* screwdriver, Figure 12.4, is used in a confined space where the longer screwdrivers cannot be used.

Figure 12.4   Stubby

The *offset* screwdriver, shown in Figure 12.5, is used to drive screws that cannot be reached with a straight screwdriver. One blade is forged in line with the shank and the other at right angles to the shank.

Figure 12.5   Offset

The standard screwdriver is also made with a *square shank,* Figure 12.6. The square shank can be used with a spanner wrench to loosen large screws that are too tight to be loosened by hand.

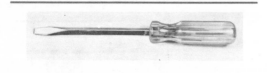

Figure 12.6   Square shank

The *Phillips* screwdriver, Figure 12.7, is a special tool that fits screw heads which have a cross slot (two slots at right angles to each other). The Phillips screwdriver will not slip and burr the end of the screw if the proper size is used. They come in several sizes.

Figure 12.7   Phillips

The *Robertson* screwdriver is made with a square blade, Figure 12.8, and comes in several sizes. The usual sizes are identified in the following table:

Size of Screw	Colour of Handle	Length of Shank
#4 to #6	Green	7.5 cm
#7 to #9	Red	8.75 cm
#10 to #14	Black	10 cm

Figure 12.8   Robertson

Pliers

Pliers are one of the most frequently used tools in the electrical trade. The basic tool requirements for electricians list seven types of pliers which gives some indication of their importance.

Types of Pliers

The *side-cutting pliers* (Figure 12.9) are a powerfully built tool for gripping, twisting, and cutting. Two sizes are used by the electrician: 15 cm and 20 cm.

Introductory Electricity

Figure 12.9   Side cutters

When cutting wire, cut straight across with an even pressure. If the wire is steel and too hard to sever with one cut, nick the wire on all sides and then place the twisting surface of the pliers on the wire adjacent to the nicks (Figure 12.10). Then, by bending the wire adjacent to the pliers, it should break off at the nicked point.

NOTE: Do not rock the wire while the cutters are making contact.

Figure 12.10   Bending wire

The *diagonal-cutting* pliers (Figure 12.11) are made for close cutting jobs, such as wire cutting while doing switchboard or fixture wiring. They are built with the cutting jaws at an angle to the side of the pliers and can be procured in lengths from 10 cm to 18 cm.

Figure 12.11   Diagonal cutters

The *round-nose pliers* (Figure 12.12) are used to make neat bends and terminal loops on wire. They are made in the 12 cm and the 15 cm size.

Figure 12.12   Round-nose pliers

The *long-nose half-round pliers* (Figure 12.13) are made for jobs that are hard to reach with the round-nose or the side-cutting pliers. Despite the long slender jaws, they are rugged tools. They are provided with side-cutting jaws. The usual lengths are 15 cm and 18 cm.

Figure 12.13   Long-nose half round pliers

The *long-nose duck-bill pliers* (Figure 12.14) have a long flat nose, tapered and beveled but without the cutters. They are useful for reaching into recesses where the flat-nose is more practical than the long-nose half-round pliers. They can be procured in the 15 cm size.

Figure 12.14   Long-nose duck-bill pliers

The *combination pliers* (Figure 12.15) are sturdy tools used for gripping and cutting. They are made with an adjustable joint for accommodating various sizes of work, yet providing high gripping strength. They are made in several sizes from about 12 cm to 24 cm in length.

Figure 12.15   Combination pliers

The *gripping pliers* (Figure 12.16) are designed to give plenty of gripping power. The sturdy jaws grip like a pipe wrench and are set at an angle for easy operation. The three position adjustable slide joint adapts them to different sizes of work. They come in the 15 cm and the 18 cm size.

Figure 12.16   Gripping pliers

Using Pliers

Select good quality pliers. They are made from alloy steel and are hardened and tempered to give long and satisfactory service. They are finished with smooth, easy riding joints and they have deeply milled teeth to provide maximum gripping power with minimum handle pressure.

The handles are non-slip and spring tempered, while the cutters are perfectly aligned and sharp.

NOTE: Pliers are also made with plastic covered handles. The plastic covers are apt to crack and present an electrical hazard.

For Review

1. Name the three main parts of a screwdriver.
2. How are screwdrivers insulated to prevent an electric shock?
3. Name three main types of screwdrivers and explain where each type is used to best advantage.
4. What precaution must be observed before using any screwdriver?
5. How is the Robertson screwdriver identified with reference to sizes?
6. (a) Name seven different types of pliers.
   (b) Where is each type best suited?
7. What precautions must be observed when using any pliers?

Experiments

Experiment 1

Objectives:
1. To prove that charges from electrified materials can be transferred to
   materials that are unelectrified
2. To prove that like charges repel one
   another
3. To prove that unlike charges attract
   one another

Materials: Two fibre pith balls with silk
attachment cords, two pith ball stands,
one cat's fur, one silk cloth, one glass
rod, one rubber rod

Procedure: Part I
1. Suspend a pith ball from each stand
   as shown in Figure 1.

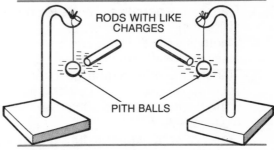

RODS WITH LIKE CHARGES

PITH BALLS

Figure 1

2. Vigorously rub the cat's fur on the
   rubber rod to obtain a negative
   charge.
3. Touch the rubber rod to one of the
   pith balls in order to transfer the
   negative charge.
4. Recharge the rubber rod and transfer the negative charge to the second pith ball.
5. Bring the two negatively charged
   pith balls close together and observe
   what happens.
6. Repeat procedures 2, 3, 4, and 5,
   but this time rub the silk on the glass
   rod to produce a positive charge.
7. Observe and record what happens
   during each step of the operation.

Procedure: Part II
1. Suspend a pith ball from each stand
   as shown in Figure 1(a).

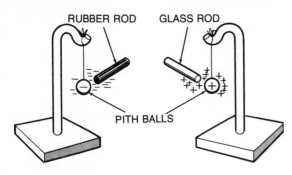

Figure 1 (a)

2. Vigorously rub the cat's fur on the rubber rod to obtain a negative charge.
3. Transfer the negative charge to one of the suspended pith balls.
4. Vigorously rub the silk cloth on the glass rod to obtain a positive charge.
5. Transfer the positive charge to the second pith ball.
6. Bring the two charged pith balls close together.
7. Observe what happens during each step of the operation.

Assignment:
1. What happened when the two pith balls with negative charges were brought together?
2. What happened when the two pith balls with positive charges were brought together?
3. What definite rule can be stated pertaining to like charges of negatively charged materials?
4. What definite rule can be stated pertaining to like charges of positively charged materials?
5. What happened when the two pith balls with opposite charges were brought together?
6. What definite rule can be stated pertaining to unlike charges?
7. Is it possible to transfer a negative charge from an electrified material to one that is unelectrified? Explain.

8. When glass and silk are rubbed together, what charge does the glass rod take?
9. What type of charge is created on the rubber rod when it is rubbed with a piece of fur?
10. What is meant by like charges?
11. What is meant by unlike charges?

Experiment 2

Objectives:
1. To construct a wet cell
2. To produce electron flow by chemical action

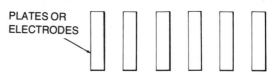

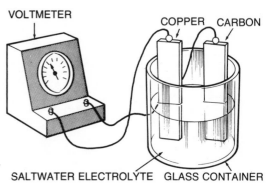

Figure 2

Materials: One conductivity cell; dc voltmeter and connecting leads, electrolyte (consisting of a solution of saltwater); plates of the following materials: carbon (C), iron (Fe), copper (Cu), zinc (Zn), brass

Procedure:
1. Make a table similar to Table 1 in your notes.
2. Prepare the electrolyte by mixing one half cup of water with one tablespoon of salt.
3. Insert a pair of dissimilar materials

(copper and carbon) and connect them to the voltmeter (Figure 2). Record the voltage in Table 1.

4. Move the plates further apart, then closer together, and observe the voltage. (Do not record.)
5. Remove the first pair of plates and, in turn, insert other pairs of dissimilar plates. For each pair follow procedures 3 and 4.
6. Remove the last pair of plates.
7. Use two strips of copper and two strips of carbon for each plate. (This doubles the area of each plate.) Insert these double strips into the container and record the voltage.

NOTE: Any two dissimilar plates can be used.

	Copper	Carbon	Zinc	Iron	Brass
Copper					
Carbon					
Zinc					
Iron					
Brass					

Table 1

Assignment:

1. What solution was used for the electrolyte?
2. Which two dissimilar materials produced the greatest voltage?
3. Which two metals produced the least voltage?
4. What two metals or materials are used for plates in the dry cell?
5. How was the voltmeter made to read in the proper direction?
6. What causes electrons to flow in the primary cell?
7. What happened to the voltage when the plates were moved closer together?
8. What happened when the plates were moved further apart?
9. What happened to the voltage when the plate size was increased?

Experiment 3

Objective: To produce electron flow by magnetism
Materials: Copper wound coil, one galvanometer, one bar magnet, connecting leads
Procedure:

1. Connect the equipment as shown in Figure 3.

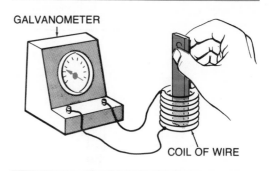

GALVANOMETER

COIL OF WIRE

Figure 3

2. With a quick motion insert the north pole of the bar magnet into the coil and observe the meter.
3. Extract the bar magnet with a quick motion and observe the meter. Figure 3 (a).

Figure 3 (a)

4. Insert the south pole of the bar magnet into the coil and observe the meter.

5. Move the magnet back and forth in the coil with quick motions and observe the meter.
6. Insert either pole of the magnet and stop its motion. Observe the meter after the magnet is held still.
7. Compare the direction of motion of the meter needle when the south pole of the magnet is inserted with the direction of needle movement when the north pole is inserted into the coil.

Figure 3 (b)

8. Compare the direction of motion of the meter needle when the south pole of the magnet is extracted from the coil with the direction of the needle movement when the north pole is extracted.

Assignment:
1. What purpose does the meter serve in this experiment?
2. (a) What three requirements are necessary to produce electron flow by magnetism?
   (b) Will electrons flow if any one of these requirements is not met? Explain.
3. Which way does the meter deflect when the south end is extracted?

4. Which way does it deflect when the north pole of the magnet is inserted into the coil? When the north end is extracted?
5. Does the polarity of the magnet and/or the direction of motion have any bearing upon the direction of electron flow? Explain.

Experiment 4

Objective: To produce electron flow by heat

Materials: One thermocouple, one galvanometer, connecting leads, source of heat (candle or propane torch)

Procedure:
1. Connect the equipment as shown in Figure 4.

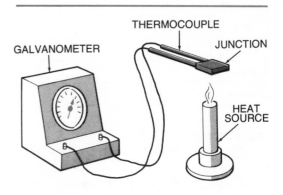

Figure 4

2. Apply heat to the junction of the two dissimilar metals.
3. Observe the deflection of the meter.
4. Allow the metal to cool and observe the deflection on the meter.

Assignment:
1. What effect was noted when heat was applied to the junction of the dissimilar metals?
2. What happened after the junction was allowed to cool?
3. What happened as the temperature was increased at the junction?

4. What types of metal were joined to-gether?
5. How are these two types of metal joined?
6. Where would this thermocouple be used in an industrial application?
7. Why are thermocouples important in industry?

Experiment 5

Objective: To produce electron flow by light

Materials: One selenium cell or sun battery, one galvanometer, source of light (flashlight), connecting leads

Procedure:
1. Connect the apparatus as shown in Figure 5. Be sure the red lead is con-nected to the positive terminal of the meter.

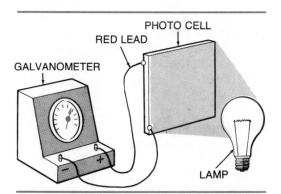

Figure 5

2. Have the light from the window or room lights directed on the cell.
3. Observe the deflection on the meter.
4. Direct a beam of light from a flash-light or a light bulb on the cell.
5. Observe the deflection on the meter.

Experiment 6

Objective: To produce electron flow by pressure

Materials: One piezoelectric crystal, one NE-51 neon lamp and socket, a piece of wood (2 cm × 2 cm × 25 cm), connecting leads

Procedure:
1. Connect the apparatus as shown in Figure 6.
2. Hold the crystal with one hand and, with the piece of wood, lightly strike the crystal. Observe the neon lamp.
3. Strike the crystal with several hard blows. Observe the neon lamp each time.

Assignment:
1. What effect was noticed when the crystal received a light blow? Ex-plain.
2. When a hard blow was applied, what effect was noticed on the neon lamp? Explain.

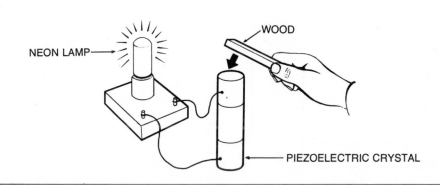

Figure 6

Experiment 7

Objective: To determine which materials are conductors and which are non-conductors

Materials: One dry cell; one 1.5 V lamp and base; connecting leads; test materials consisting of: copper, aluminum, brass, glass, bakelite, rubber, plastic, mica, iron, zinc, silver, lead, and nickel (Use a Canadian nickel.)

Procedure:
1. Make a table similar to Table 2 in your notes.
2. Connect the circuit as in Figure 7.

Material	
Conductor	**Non-conductor**

Table 2

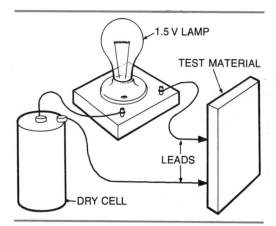

Figure 7

3. Touch the two leads together to see if there is a complete circuit. (The lamp will light if the circuit is complete. This indicates that the test material is a conductor. If the lamp does not light, this will indicate that the material is a non-conductor.)

Assignment:
1. What did you determine about all the metals that were tested?
2. Which materials would be classed as non-conductors?
3. Give a definition for:
   (a) a conductor
   (b) a non-conductor

Experiment 8

Objectives:
1. To prove that an increase in pressure (voltage) causes an increase in electron flow (resistance remains constant)
2. To prove that a decrease in resistance causes an increase in electron flow (voltage remains constant)

Materials: 0-1 dc ammeter; 0-150 dc voltmeter; 25, 40, 60, 100 W lamps; connecting leads; dc source of supply

Procedure: Part I
1. Make tables similar to Tables 3 and 4 in your notes.
2. Connect the circuit as shown in Figure 8 and insert a 100 W lamp.

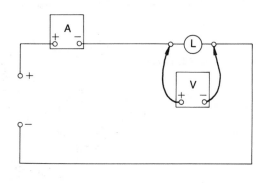

Figure 8

Introductory Electricity

3. Apply about 20 V to the circuit and increase the voltage in five steps to 120 V. Observe and record the meter readings for each step in Table 3.
4. Now decrease the voltage in five steps and observe the readings on the meters.

Lamp watts	Volts	Amperes

Table 3

Procedure: Part II
1. Remove the 100 W lamp and insert a 25 W lamp.
2. Apply 120 dc volts to the circuit.
3. Observe and record the readings on the meters.
4. Leave the circuit connected to 120 V and in turn insert a 40 W lamp, 60 W lamp, and 100 W lamp and for each observe and record the readings on the meters in Table 4.

Lamp watts	Volts	Amperes	Ohms

Table 4

Assignment:
1. When the voltage was increased and the resistance remained constant, what happened to the electron flow?
2. When the voltage was decreased, what happened to the electron flow?

3. When the resistance was decreased and the voltage remained constant, what happened to the electron flow?
4. Which lamp draws the most electron flow? Why?
5. Calculate the resistance of each lamp ($R = E/I$) and record in Table 4.
6. Which lamp has the least resistance? Why?
7. From the results of the above experiment, write a statement for Ohm's Law.

Experiment 9

Objective: To show the heating effect of electron flow (current flow) in a wire
Materials: Test board, 0-15 dc ammeter; SPST switch; three 150 W lamps; two 650 W cone heaters; test samples of No. 28, 30, 32, and 34 cotton-covered copper wire; connecting leads
Procedure:
1. Connect the circuit as in Figure 9 and apply a voltage of about 120 V.

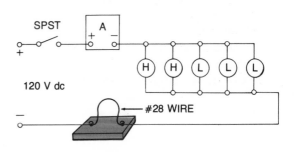

Figure 9

NOTE: Do not touch any of the lamps or cone heaters after insertion.
2. Insert a 150 W lamp.
3. Close the switch and observe the ammeter.
4. Insert, one at a time at 15 second intervals, the 150 W lamps and the two 650 W cone heaters until something burns.

5. Observe the ammeter each time and record.
6. Repeat the experiment using, in turn, each of the other copper wires and record your observations each time.

Assignment:
1. What noticeable effect has electron flow (current) on a wire?
2. What noticeable effect is produced when the electron flow (current) is increased?
3. What will eventually happen to a wire if the current is increased beyond its capacity?
4. Which size of wire carried the most current? Why?
5. How can you protect the wiring from overheating?
6. What is the danger of the overheating of a wire in your home?

Experiment 10

Objective: To show the action and purpose of a plug fuse
Materials: Six 150 W lamps, 0-15 dc ammeter, lamp boards, 3 A plug fuses, connecting leads
Procedure:
1. Make a table similar to Table 5 in your notes.
2. Connect the circuit as in Figure 10.

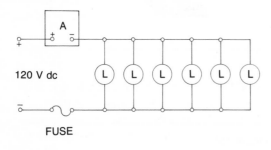

Figure 10

3. Insert a 3 A plug fuse and apply a voltage of about 120 V.

4. Insert three 150 W lamps. This will load the circuit to the rating of the fuse (3 A).
5. Add one more 150 W lamp and wait 10 seconds. If the fuse does not blow, add one lamp at a time in 10-second intervals, until the fuse blows. Record the amount of time it took for the fuse to blow in Table 5.
6. Insert another good 3 A fuse with the same number of lamps in the circuit and record the length of time and the number of amperes required to blow the fuse. Record in Table 5.

Type of fuse or breaker	Ampere rating	Average amperes	Average seconds

Table 5

Assignment:
1. State the purpose of the fuse.
2. Why are fuses enclosed?
3. When would a good fuse not be of any use in a circuit?·
4. A #14 AWG wire has a capacity of 15 A. What size fuse would you use to protect the circuit?
5. Your home branch circuits are protected by a 15 A fuse. If this fuse burned out and no 15 A fuses were available, what would you use to protect the circuit?

Experiment 11

Objectives:
1. To observe the nature of natural magnets
2. To observe the magnetic field around a natural magnet
3. To observe the attraction of natural magnets

Materials: Lodestones, iron filings, compasses
Procedure: Part I
1. Obtain a piece of lodestone.

2. Sprinkle iron filings on a piece of paper and bring the natural magnet close to the filings (Figure 11).
3. Observe what takes place.

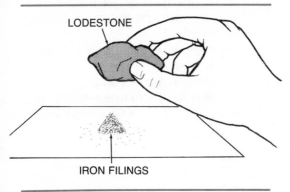

Figure 11

Assignment:
1. Make a neat diagram in your notebook showing the effect on iron filings when they are brought near a piece of lodestone.

Procedure: Part II
1. Obtain a second piece of lodestone and bring it near the first (Figure 11(a)).
2. Observe what takes place.

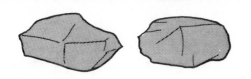

Figure 11 (a)

Procedure: Part III
1. Place a piece of lodestone on the top of the bench.
2. Obtain a small compass and slowly move the compass around the stationary piece of lodestone (Figure 11 (b)).

Assignment:
1. Make a neat diagram showing the effect of rotating a compass around a piece of lodestone.

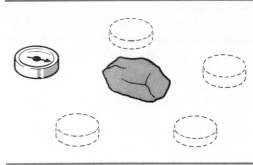

Figure 11 (b)

Experiment 12

Objectives:
1. To observe the field around a bar magnet
2. To observe the field around a horse-shoe magnet

Materials: Bar magnet, horseshoe magnet, two sheets of unlined paper, container of iron filings

Procedure: Part I
1. Place the bar magnet on the bench.
2. Cover the magnet with a sheet of unlined paper (Figure 12).

Figure 12

3. Sprinkle iron filings on the paper and tap lightly with a pencil.
4. Observe the field pattern of the lines of force around a bar magnet.

Assignment:

1. Make a neat full-page diagram of the field pattern in your notes.
2. Where do most of the iron filings settle? Explain.

Procedure: Part II

1. Place the horseshoe magnet on the bench.
2. Cover the magnet with a sheet of unlined paper (Figure 12 (a)).

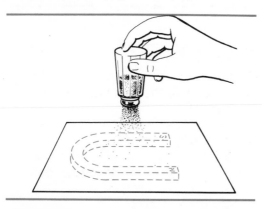

Figure 12 (a)

3. Sprinkle iron filings on the paper and tap lightly with a pencil.
4. Observe the field pattern of the lines of force around a horseshoe magnet.

Assignment:

1. Make a neat full-page diagram of the field pattern in your notes.
2. Where do most of the iron filings settle? Explain.

Experiment 13

Objectives:

1. To observe the effects of attraction and repulsion
2. To prove the law of like and unlike poles
3. To observe the fields where like poles are concerned
4. To observe the fields where unlike poles are concerned

Materials: Two bar magnets, iron filings, two sheets of unlined paper

Procedure:

1. Bring two north poles together and note the effect.
2. Bring two south poles together and note the effect.
3. Bring two unlike poles together and note the effect.
4. Lay two bar magnets on the bench with like poles 2 cm apart and cover with a sheet of paper (Figure 13).

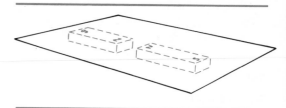

Figure 13

5. Sprinkle iron filings on the paper, tap lightly with a pencil, and observe what takes place.
6. Reverse one magnet so that unlike poles are opposite to each other and cover with a sheet of paper (Figure 13 (a)).

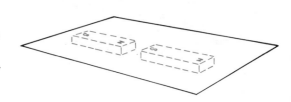

Figure 13 (a)

7. Sprinkle iron filings on the paper, tap lightly with a pencil, and observe what takes place.

Assignment:

1. What happened when like poles were brought together? Explain.
2. What happened when unlike poles were brought together? Explain.

3. Make two neat drawings showing the field pattern of like and unlike poles placed opposite to each other.
4. Explain the field pattern formed when like poles are placed opposite to each other.
5. Explain the field pattern formed when unlike poles are placed opposite to each other.

Experiment 14

Objectives: To observe magnetic lines and magnetic fields around horseshoe magnets with:
1. Unlike poles
2. Like poles

Materials: Two horseshoe magnets, iron filings, two sheets of unlined paper

Procedure:
1. Lay two horseshoe magnets on the bench with the unlike poles 2 cm apart and cover with a sheet of paper (Figure 14).

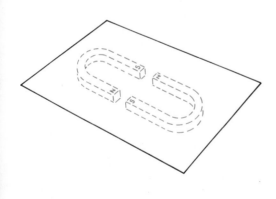

Figure 14

2. Sprinkle iron filings on the paper, tap lightly with a pencil, and observe what takes place.
3. Reverse one magnet so that like poles are opposite to each other and cover with a sheet of paper (Figure 14 (a)).

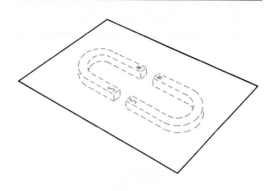

Figure 14 (a)

4. Sprinkle iron filings on the paper, tap lightly with a pencil, and observe what takes place.

Assignment:
1. Make two neat drawings showing the field pattern of like and unlike poles placed opposite to each other.
2. Explain the field pattern formed when unlike poles are placed opposite to each other.
3. Explain the field pattern formed when like poles are placed opposite to each other.

Experiment 15

Objective: To plot, with the use of a compass, the direction and range of the magnetic lines of force (*flux lines*) around a bar magnet

Materials: Bar magnet, compass, sheet of unlined paper

Procedure:
1. With the compass, determine the polarity of the bar magnet.
2. Place the sheet of unlined paper on the bench.
3. Place the bar magnet in the centre of the sheet and trace its outline (Figure 15). *Leave the magnet in this position.*
4. Mark points around the magnet as shown in Figure 15. The points should be about 1 cm apart.

5. Starting at the north pole, place the compass at point one. The back of the arrow (S pole) should point to point one (Figure 15).

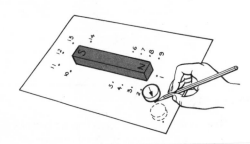

Figure 15

6. Mark a point at the end of the arrow.
7. Shift the compass until the back of the arrow points to this marked point.
8. Mark another point at the end of the arrow.
9. Continue this procedure until you reach the south pole or leave the paper.
10. Join all the plotted points with a pencil and draw an arrow on this line to show the flux direction.
11. Repeat the same procedure for the other marked points.
NOTE: When plotting points at the south pole, the compass arrow (N pole) will point to the south end of the magnet.

Experiment 16

Objective: To plot, with the use of a compass, the direction and range of the magnetic lines of force around a horseshoe magnet
Materials: Horseshoe magnet, compass, sheet of unlined paper

Procedure:
1. With the compass, determine the polarity of the horseshoe magnet.
2. Place the sheet of unlined paper on the bench.
3. Place the horseshoe magnet closer to one end of the sheet and trace its outline (Figure 16). *Leave the magnet in this position.*

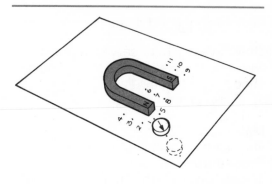

Figure 16

4. Mark points around each pole as shown in Figure 16. The points should be about 1 cm apart.
5. Starting at the north pole, place the compass at point one. The back of the arrow (S pole) should point to point one (Figure 16).
6. Mark a point at the end of the arrow.
7. Shift the compass until the back of the arrow points to this marked point.
8. Mark another point at the end of the arrow.
9. Continue this procedure until you reach the south pole or leave the paper.
10. Join all the plotted points with a pencil and draw an arrow on this line to show the flux direction.
11. Repeat the same procedure for the other marked points.
NOTE: When plotting points at the south pole, the compass arrow (N pole) will point to the south end of the magnet.

Experiment 17

Objective: To make a magnet by induction

Materials: Compass, bar magnet, iron filings, two nails

Procedure:

1. Test one of the nails for magnetism by inserting the point into a pile of iron filings (Figure 17).

Figure 17

2. Place the point of the nail into the pile of iron filings and bring one end of the magnet into contact with the head of the nail (Figure 17 (a)).

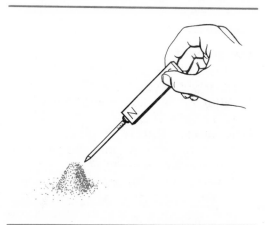

Figure 17 (a)

3. Remove the magnet from the nail and observe what happens.
4. Test the second nail for magnetism.
5. Stroke the nail as shown in Figure 17 (b).
6. Make another test for magnetism.

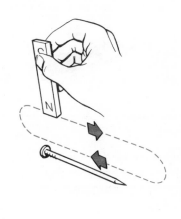

Figure 17 (b)

Assignment:

1. When the nail was inserted into the iron filings was there any attraction? Explain.
2. With the bar magnet placed at the nail head was there any attraction? Explain.
3. After the nail was stroked was there any attraction? Explain.
4. What is meant by magnetic induction?

Experiment 18

Objectives:

1. To determine which metal makes the stronger magnet
2. To make a consequent pole magnet

Materials: Two bar magnets, two 1 cm × 15 cm strips of soft iron, 15 cm piece of hacksaw blade, iron filings

Procedure: **Part 1**

1. Lay a piece of soft iron flat on the bench.

2. With a bar magnet, stroke it 10 times as shown in Figure 18.

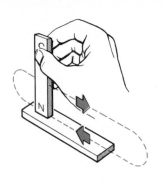

Figure 18

3. Dip each end of the soft iron into iron filings and observe the amount of iron filings attracted.
4. Remove the iron filings and leave the soft iron for about 5 minutes and then test again for attraction of the iron filings. Observe.

Procedure: Part II

1. Lay a piece of hard steel (hacksaw blade) flat on the bench.
2. Give it 10 strokes with a bar magnet as shown in Figure 18 (a).

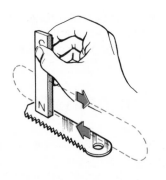

Figure 18 (a)

3. Dip each end of the hard steel into iron filings and observe the amount of iron filings attracted.

4. Remove the iron filings and leave the hard steel for about 5 minutes and then test again for attraction of the iron filings. Observe.

Assignment:

1. How did the attraction of iron filings compare between the soft iron and hard steel?
2. After putting the metals aside for a few minutes, which metal retained the most magnetism? Explain.
3. Which metal would be better suited for a permanent magnet? Why?
4. What principle was involved in magnetizing the metals?

Procedure: Part III

1. Lay the same piece of soft iron flat on the bench.
2. Stroke it 10 times with a bar magnet as in Figure 18 (b).
3. With a compass, determine the polarity of the ends at which you started and finished.

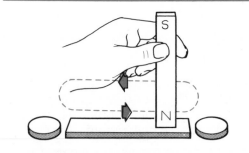

Figure 18 (b)

Assignment:

1. What polarity did the end of the iron have where you started?
2. What polarity did the end have where you finished? Explain.

Procedure: Part IV

1. Lay another unmagnetized piece of soft iron flat on the table.
2. Using two bar magnets, stroke them 10 times as shown in Figure 18 (c).
3. With a compass, test the strip of iron at each end and at the centre for polarity. Observe.

Introductory Electricity

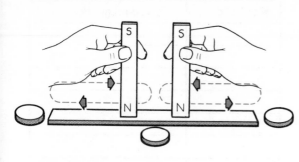

Figure 18 (c)

Assignment:
1. What polarities were found on the iron when both magnets were used? Explain.
2. What is the centre pole called?

Experiment 19

Objective: To show proof of the molecular theory of magnetism
Materials: Test tube, iron filings, compass, hacksaw blade, bar magnet
Procedure: Part I
1. Half fill the test tube with iron filings.
2. Shake the test tube and note how the iron filings lie in all directions.
3. Test each end of the test tube with a compass to determine if there is any polarity.
4. Draw the magnet along the test tube (Figure 19).

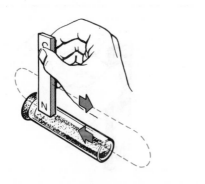

Figure 19

5. Test each end of the test tube with the compass to determine if there is any polarity. *(Be careful not to disturb the filings in the test tube.)*
6. Shake the test tube and again test for polarity.

Assignment:
1. Was there any polarity before stroking the test tube? Why?
2. Was there any polarity after stroking the test tube? Explain.
3. What happened to the polarity when the test tube was shaken? Explain.

Procedure: Part II
1. Magnetize the hacksaw blade by stroking it 10 times with the bar magnet (Figure 19 (a)).

Figure 19 (a)

2. With the compass test each end of the hacksaw blade for polarity.
3. Break the hacksaw blade into two pieces. Again test each piece for polarity.
4. Dip each piece into iron filings. Observe the amount of filings attracted.
5. Break the two pieces of hacksaw blade in half. Test each for polarity.
6. Dip each piece into iron filings. Observe the amount of filings attracted.
7. Break each of the four pieces of hacksaw blade in half. Test each piece for polarity.
8. Dip each piece into iron filings. Observe the amount of iron filings attracted.

Assignment:

1. After breaking the hacksaw blade into two pieces, did each piece have polarity? Why?
2. After breaking the hacksaw blade into several pieces, did each piece have polarity? Explain.
3. Was there any difference in the amount of attraction in each piece as it was broken into smaller pieces? Explain.

Experiment 20

Objective: To determine which metals are magnetic and which are non-magnetic

Materials: Bar magnet; testing materials: steel, iron, nickel, copper, aluminum, brass, silver, lead, gold, zinc, and stainless steel

Procedure:

1. Make a table similar to Table 6 in your notes.
2. With the bar magnet, test each metal in turn to determine whether it is magnetic or non-magnetic (Figure 20). (If the metal is attracted to the magnet, it is magnetic; if it is not, it is non-magnetic.)

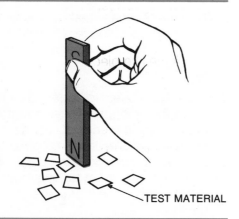

TEST MATERIAL

Figure 20

3. List the magnetic and non-magnetic metals in Table 6.

Magnetic	Non-magnetic

Table 6

Assignment:

1. What is meant by a magnetic material?
2. Define a non-magnetic material.
3. Name three magnetic metals.
4. List six non-magnetic metals.

Experiment 21

Objective: To observe the effects of laminating magnets

Materials: Three bar magnets, ten soft-iron bars (0.5 cm × 2 cm × 2 cm)

Procedure:

1. Place the iron bars on the table.
2. Dip the north end of a bar magnet into the iron bars and record the number of bars attracted (Figure 21).

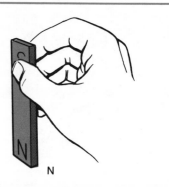

N

Figure 21

3. Dip two magnets with north poles together into the iron bars and record the number of bars attracted (Figure 21 (a)).

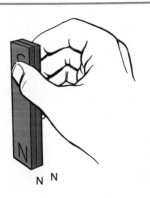

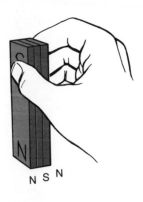

Figure 21 (a)

Figure 21 (c)

4. Dip three magnets with north poles together into the iron bars and record the number of bars attracted (Figure 21 (b)).

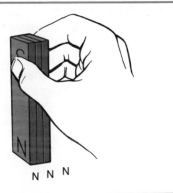

Figure 21 (b)

5. Reverse the centre magnet so that a south pole is between the two north poles and dip into the iron bars. Record the number of bars attracted (Figure 21 (c)).

Assignment:
1. How many bars were attracted when one magnet was used?
2. When two north poles were used, how did the number of bars attracted compare with one magnet being used?
3. What was the result when three north magnets were used?
4. Was there a marked difference when more north magnets were used? Explain.
5. How many bars were attracted when the centre was reversed?
6. Why did this difference occur?
7. Make a neat diagram to illustrate the field pattern in Figure 21 (b).
8. Make a neat diagram to show the lines of force in Figure 21 (c).

Experiment 22

Objective: To determine which materials are most suitable for magnetic screening (shielding)

Materials: Bar magnet; ten iron paper clips; sheets of copper, lead, zinc, aluminum, brass, glass, masonite, stainless steel, soft iron, and steel

Procedure:
1. Make a table similar to Table 7 in your notes.
2. Place the iron paper clips on the bench (Figure 22).

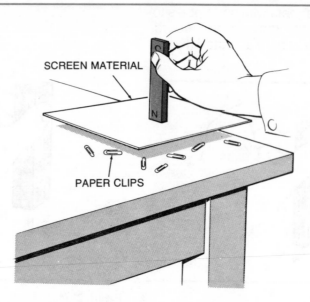

SCREEN MATERIAL

PAPER CLIPS

Figure 22

3. Place the screen material over the clips.
4. Slowly bring the magnet to the screen material (Figure 22) and record the number of clips attracted.
5. Repeat the same procedure using the different screen materials and record your observations in Table 7.

Screen material	Amount attracted

Table 7

Assignment:
1. Which materials did the most effective screening? Explain.
2. Which metal would be best as a screen or protective material against magnetic lines? Why?
3. Will magnetic lines pass through all non-magnetic materials? Explain.
4. What prevents magnetic lines from passing through iron or nickel?
5. State three places where magnetic screening is used.
6. Draw a neat diagram showing how a meter can be shielded.

Experiment 23

Objectives:
1. To show how to connect a voltmeter
2. To connect and measure the voltage of dry cells connected in series
3. To connect and measure the voltage of dry cells connected in parallel

Materials: Three #6 dry cells, voltmeter 0-10 V dc, SPST switch, connecting leads

Procedure: Part I

1. Make tables similar to Tables 8 and 9 in your notes.
2. Connect one dry cell as in Figure 23.

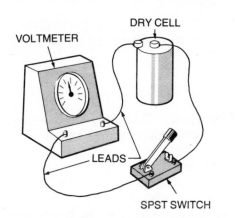

Figure 23

3. Close the SPST switch. Measure and record the voltage in Table 8.
4. Open the SPST switch. Connect two dry cells in series (Figure 23 (a)).

No. of cells	Volts

Table 8 — Series

No. of cells	Volts

Table 9 — Parallel

6. Open the SPST switch. Connect three dry cells in series (Figure 23 (b)).
7. Close the switch. Measure and record the voltage in Table 8.
8. Open the switch. Disconnect the circuit.

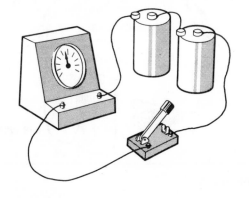

Figure 23 (a)

5. Close the SPST switch. Measure and record the voltage in Table 8.

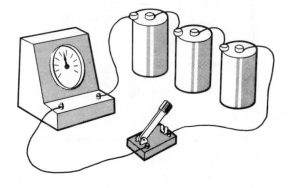

Figure 23 (b)

Procedure: Part II

1. Connect two dry cells in parallel as in Figure 23 (c).

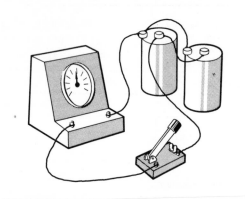

Figure 23 (c)

2. Close the SPST switch. Measure and record the voltage in Table 9.
3. Open the SPST switch. Connect three dry cells in parallel as in Figure 23 (d).

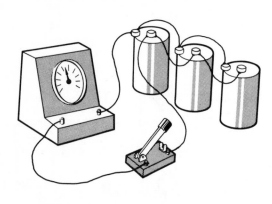

Figure 23 (d)

4. Close the SPST switch. Measure and record the voltage in Table 9.
5. Open the switch. Disconnect the circuit.

Assignment:

1. How is the voltmeter connected in the circuit?

2. What happened to the voltage as each dry cell was connected in series?
3. Make a statement regarding the total voltage of dry cells connected in series.
4. What happened to the voltage as each dry cell was connected in parallel?
5. Make a statement regarding the total voltage of dry cells connected in parallel.

Experiment 24

Objective: To show the presence of a magnetic field around a current-carrying conductor

Materials: Two dry cells or a dc source of power, #18 T.W. wire, SPST switch, iron filings, single conductor stand, connecting leads, plastic sheet

NOTE: Do not close the SPST switch for any longer than five seconds at one time.

Procedure: Part I

1. Connect the equipment as shown in Figure 24.

IRON FILINGS

#18 WIRE

Figure 24

2. With the switch open, test the conductor for a magnetic field by dipping it into the iron filings.
3. Close the switch and test again. Observe.

Assignment:

1. Make a diagram showing the effect of dipping a current-carrying conductor into iron filings.

Procedure: Part II

1. Connect the equipment as shown in Figure 24 (a).

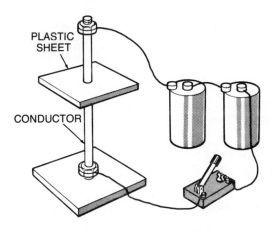

Figure 24 (a)

2. With the switch open, sprinkle iron filings onto the plastic sheet and tap with a pencil. Observe if there is a field pattern.
3. Close the switch and again tap the plastic sheet with a pencil. Observe.

Assignment:

1. Make a diagram showing the field pattern of a current-carrying conductor.
2. Did the iron filings form a pattern when no current was flowing in the conductor? Why?

Experiment 25

Objectives:

1. To determine the direction of lines of force around a current-carrying conductor.
2. To show proof of the Left-Hand Rule for a current-carrying conductor

Materials: Single conductor stand, connecting leads, two dry cells or a dc source of power, SPST switch, compass, plastic sheet

NOTE: Do not close the SPST switch for any longer than five seconds at one time.

Procedure: Part I

1. Connect the equipment as shown in Figure 25.

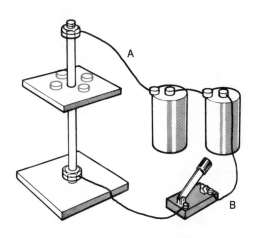

Figure 25

2. Determine the direction of current flow (from the negative terminal).
3. Close the switch and move the compass around the single conductor on the plastic sheet.
4. Observe the direction in which the needle points.

Assignment:

1. From which terminal of the dry cell does the current flow?
2. Make a neat drawing showing the direction of the compass needles around the conductor (Figure 25).
3. Which end of the compass needle points in the direction of the flux?

Procedure: Part II

1. Interchange wires A and B on the dry cell (Figure 25 (a)).
2. Determine the direction of current flow.

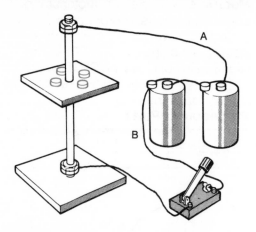

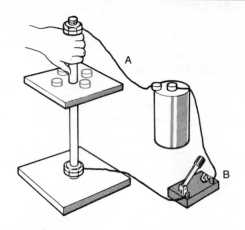

Figure 25 (a)

Figure 25 (b)

3. Close the switch and move the compass around the single conductor on the plastic sheet and observe the direction in which the needle points.

Assignment:

1. Make a neat drawing showing the direction of the compass needles around the conductor (Figure 25 (a)).
2. Does the direction of the current flow have a definite bearing on the direction of flux? Explain.

Procedure: Part III

1. Connect the equipment as shown in Figure 25 (b).
2. Wrap the left hand around the conductor as indicated in Figure 25 (b). Close the switch and observe the direction in which the needle points.
3. Open the switch and reverse the current by interchanging wires A and B on the dry cell.
4. Repeat procedure 2.

Assignment:

1. Write the Left-Hand Rule for a current carrying conductor.
2. Explain the results of this experiment with reference to proof of the Left-Hand Rule.

Experiment 26

Objective: To determine the magnetic field around a coil of wire

Materials: Helix board, dry cells or a dc source of power, SPST switch, compass, connecting leads

NOTE: Do not close the SPST switch for any longer than five seconds at one time.

Procedure:

1. Connect the apparatus as shown in Figure 26.

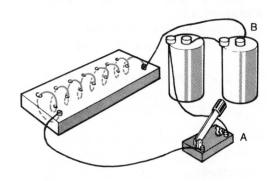

Figure 26

2. Sprinkle iron filings on the plastic plate around the coil.

3. Close the SPST switch and gently tap the plate. Observe.
4. Open the SPST switch.
5. Remove the iron filings and place a compass at one end of the coil. Close the SPST switch and observe the direction in which the needle points.
6. Place the compass in different positions around the coil and inside the coil and close the SPST switch each time. Observe the needle direction each time.
7. Open the SPST switch. Reverse the current by interchanging wires A and B on the dry cells.
8. Again place the compass in different positions around and inside the coil and close the switch each time and observe.
9. Using the Left-Hand Rule prove the polarity of the coil.

Assignment:
1. Make a neat drawing showing the field pattern produced when current flowed through the coil.
2. To what other field pattern is this field pattern similar?
3. With the current flowing in the direction shown in Figure 26, mark the polarity on your drawing.
4. What happened to the polarity of the coil when the current was reversed?
5. In which direction did the compass needle point when it was outside the coil? Inside the coil?

Experiment 27

Objectives:
1. To make an electromagnet
2. To observe the effects of an electromagnet

Materials: 5 mm × 15 cm soft-iron rod, copper or brass rod, SPST switch, #20 insulated copper wire, dry cell or dc source of power, connecting leads, ten iron paper clips.

NOTE: Do not close the SPST switch for any longer than five seconds at one time.

Procedure: Part I
1. Wind 20 turns of the insulated wire onto the iron rod (Figure 27).

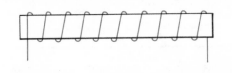

Figure 27

2. Dip each end of the iron rod into the clips and observe.

Procedure: Part II
1. Connect a dry cell and an SPST switch to the wire. (Figure 27 (a)).

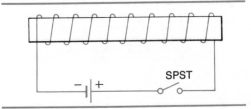

SPST

Figure 27 (a)

2. Dip each end of the iron rod into the clips and at the same time close the SPST switch. Observe the number of iron clips attracted.
3. Reverse the direction of current flow to the electromagnet (Figure 27 (b)).

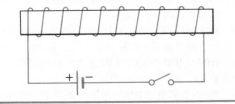

Figure 27 (b)

4. Again dip each end of the iron rod into the clips and at the same time close the SPST switch. Observe the number of clips attracted.

Procedure: Part III

1. Remove the iron rod from the coil (Figure 27 (c)).

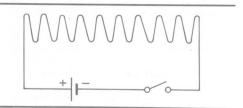

Figure 27 (c)

2. Dip each end of the coil into the iron clips and at the same time press the SPST switch. Observe the number of iron clips attracted.

Procedure: Part IV

1. Insert a copper or brass rod into the coil (Figure 27 (d)).

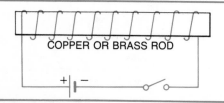

COPPER OR BRASS ROD

Figure 27 (d)

2. Dip each end of the rod into the iron clips and at the same time close the SPST switch. Observe the number of clips attracted.

Assignment:

1. In Part I, did the iron rod attract any iron clips? Explain.
2. In Part II, did the iron rod attract any iron clips? Explain.
3. Was there any noticeable difference in the number of iron clips attracted when the current was reversed? Why?
4. How did the number of iron clips attracted by the open coil magnet of Part III compare with the iron-core electromagnet? Explain.
5. In Part IV, how did the number of iron clips attracted by the rod compare with the open coil? Explain.

Experiment 28

Objective: To show proof of the Left-Hand Rule for electromagnets (solenoids)

Materials: Iron rod, SPST switch, #20 insulated copper wire, dry cell, compass, connecting leads

Procedure:

1. Make a neat drawing of Figure 28 in your notes.

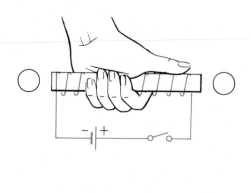

Figure 28

2. Connect the equipment as shown in Figure 28.
3. Close the switch and wrap your fingers around the rod as in Figure 28 and observe the compass needle.
4. Open the SPST switch.
5. Reverse the current through the coil by interchanging the leads on the dry cell.
6. Close the switch and apply the Left-Hand Rule and observe the compass needle.
7. Open the switch.

Assignment:

1. Record your observations for this experiment on your drawing (Figure 28).
2. Write a summary for this experiment with reference to proof of the Left-Hand Rule for electromagnets.

Experiment 29

Objectives:
1. To determine the polarity of electro-magnets (solenoids)
2. To show how to reverse the polarity of electromagnets
3. To make a consequent pole elec-tromagnet

Materials: 5 mm × 15 cm iron rod, SPST switch, #20 insulated copper wire, dry cell, compass, connecting leads

NOTE: Do not close the SPST switch for any longer than five seconds at one time.

Procedure: Part I
1. Make neat drawings of Figures 29 to 29 (d) in your notes.
2. Wind 20 turns of insulated wire onto the iron rod and connect as in Figure 29.

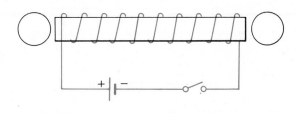

Figure 29 (a)

Assignment:
1. Record your observations for this experiment on your drawings of Fig-ures 29 and 29 (a).
2. What happened to the polarity of the electromagnet when the current was reversed? Explain.

Procedure: Part II
1. Rewind the 20 turns of insulated wire in the opposite direction around the iron rod and connect as in Figure 29 (b).

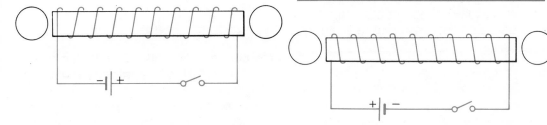

Figure 29

Figure 29 (b)

3. Place the compass at one end of the iron rod.
4. Close the SPST switch and observe the direction in which the compass needle points.
5. Place the compass at the other end of the iron rod.
6. Close the SPST switch and observe the direction in which the compass needle points.
7. Reverse the direction of the current flow (Figure 29 (a)).
8. Repeat steps 3 to 6.

2. Place the compass at one end of the iron rod.
3. Close the SPST switch and observe the direction in which the compass needle points.
4. Place the compass at the other end of the iron rod.
5. Close the SPST switch and observe the direction in which the compass needle points.
6. Reverse the direction of the current flow (Figure 29 (c)).
7. Repeat steps 2 to 5.

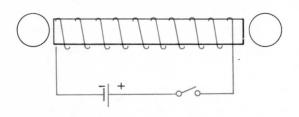

Figure 29 (c)

Assignment:
1. Record your observations for this experiment on your drawings of Figures 29 (b) and 29 (c).
2. What happened to the polarity when the coil was wound in the opposite direction? Explain.
3. What happened to the polarity when the current was reversed? Why?

Procedure: Part III
1. Wind 10 turns of insulated wire onto the centre of the iron rod in one direction, form a loop, and wind 10 more turns in the opposite direction. Connect as in Figure 29 (d).

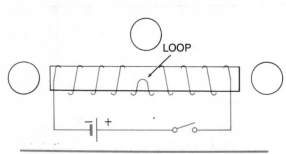

LOOP

Figure 29 (d)

2. Place a compass at one end of the iron rod. Close the SPST switch and observe the direction in which the compass needle points.
3. Place the compass at the other end of the rod. Close the SPST switch and observe the direction in which the compass needle points.
4. Open the SPST switch.

5. Reverse the current by interchanging the wires on the dry cell.
6. Repeat steps 2 and 3. Observe and record for each step.
7. Open the SPST switch.
8. Place the compass at the middle of the rod (Figure 29 (d)). Close the SPST switch and observe the direction in which the compass needle points.
9. Reverse the current by interchanging the wires on the dry cell.
10. Repeat steps 2 and 3. Observe and record for each step.
11. Open the SPST switch.

Assignment:
1. Record your observations for this experiment on your drawing of Figure 29 (d).
2. What name is given to the centre pole?
3. What happened to the polarity when the current was reversed?

Experiment 30

Objective: To determine the factors which control the strength of electromagnets

Materials: Iron rod, copper or brass rod, #20 insulated copper wire, dry cell, iron paper clips, connecting leads, SPST switch

NOTE: Do not close the SPST switch for any longer than five seconds at one time.

Procedure: Part I
1. Wrap 15 turns of insulated wire around the iron rod and connect the circuit, as in Figure 30.
2. Close the SPST switch and insert one end of the electromagnet into the iron clips. Observe and record the number of iron clips attracted.

Procedure: Part II
1. Add another dry cell in series to the circuit (Figure 30 (a)).

Introductory Electricity

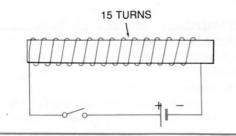

15 TURNS

Figure 30

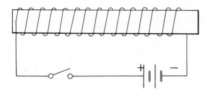

Figure 30 (a)

2. Close the SPST switch and insert one end of the electromagnet into the iron clips. Observe and record the number of iron clips attracted.

Procedure: Part III

1. Wrap 30 turns of insulated wire around the iron rod and connect the circuit as in Figure 30 (b).

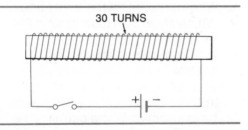

30 TURNS

Figure 30 (b)

2. Close the SPST switch and insert one end of the electromagnet into the iron clips. Observe and record the number of iron clips attracted.

Procedure: Part IV

1. Add another dry cell in series to the circuit and connect as in Figure 30 (c).

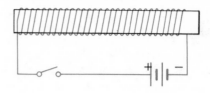

Figure 30 (c)

2. Close the SPST switch and insert one end of the electromagnet into the iron clips. Observe and record the number of iron clips attracted.

Procedure: Part V

1. Remove the iron rod and insert a brass or copper rod (Figure 30 (d)).

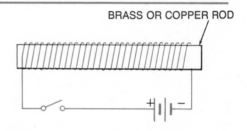

BRASS OR COPPER ROD

Figure 30 (d)

2. Close the SPST switch and insert the electromagnet into the iron clips. Observe and record the number of iron clips attracted.

Assignment:

1. What happened to the number of iron clips attracted when you increased the current through the electromagnet? Explain.
2. What effect did an increase in the number of turns have on the number of iron clips attracted? Explain.
3. When a brass or copper rod was used in place of iron, did it affect the strength of the electromagnet?
4. Name four factors which affect the strength of an electromagnet and explain how each affects the strength.

Project #1

Objective: To wire a simple bell circuit
Materials: One bell, one dry cell, one push button, #18 T.W. wire, bell wiring board
Procedure:
1. Arrange the bell, dry cell, and push button as shown in Figure 1. Space each neatly.

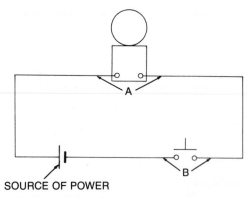

SOURCE OF POWER

Figure 1

2. Using #18 T.W. bell wire, wire the circuit as connected in Figure 1.
3. Make the wire neat and square on the bell board.
4. Have the instructor check the circuit.

Assignment:
1. What is meant by the term circuit?
2. Which section of the circuit is the feed?
3. Which section of the circuit is the control?
4. Why is this section called the control?
5. Which section of the circuit is the return?
6. How could the simple circuit be used to test for conductors or insulators?
7. How many paths for current flow are there in this circuit?
8. Make a neat drawing of Figure 1 in your notes and indicate by arrows the direction of current flow.

Projects

9. What is the voltage of the dry cell in Figure 1?
10. If the bell did not ring after connecting the circuit as in Figure 1, what procedure would you use to test the circuit?
11. If a jumper wire were connected across the push button as shown at B, how would the circuit function? Explain.
12. If a jumper wire were connected across the bell as shown at A, would the bell ring? Why?

Project #2

Objective: To wire two bells in series and controlled by one push button
Materials: Two bells, one push button, one dry cell, #18 T.W. bell wire
Procedure:
1. Make a neat drawing of Figure 2 (a) in your notes.
2. Now study the completed diagram of Figure 2 and complete the diagram of Figure 2 (a). Connect the bells in series.

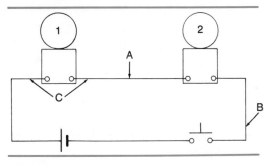

Figure 2

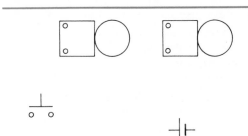

Figure 2 (a)

3. Wire the circuit of Figure 2.
4. Have the circuit checked by the instructor.
5. Test the circuit.

Assignment:
1. What is meant by a series circuit?
2. Place arrows showing the direction of current flow in the completed diagram of Figure 2 (a).
3. In Figure 2, if one bell were burned out, would the other operate? Explain.
4. If the circuit were broken at point A, which bell would operate? Why?
5. If the circuit were broken at point B, which bell would operate? Why?
6. If a wire were connected across bell #1 as shown at C, which bell would operate? Explain.
7. If only one bell operates in the series circuit of two bells, state the reason.
8. Draw a neat schematic diagram of four bells connected in series and controlled by one push button using two dry cells in series.
9. In the circuit of Question 8, how much voltage does each bell take? Explain.

Project #3

Objective: To wire one bell controlled by two push buttons in series
Materials: One bell, two push buttons, dry cell, #18 T.W. wire
Procedure:
1. Make a neat drawing of Figure 3 (a) in your notes.
2. Now study the completed diagram of Figure 3 and complete the diagram of Figure 3 (a).
3. Wire the circuit of Figure 3.
4. Have the circuit checked by the instructor.
5. Test the circuit.

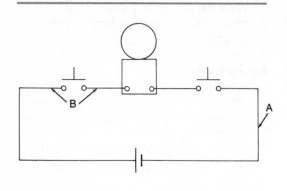

Figure 3

Project #4

Objective: To wire two bells in parallel controlled by one push button
Materials: Two bells, one push button, one dry cell, #18 T.W. bell wire
Procedure:
1. Make a neat drawing of Figure 4 (a) in your notes.
2. Now study the completed diagram of Figure 4 and complete the diagram of Figure 4 (a). Connect the bells in parallel.

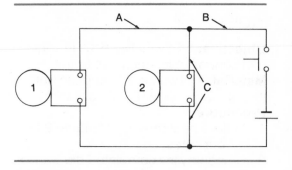

Figure 4

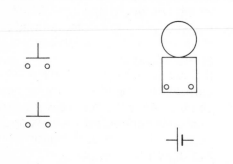

Figure 3 (a)

Assignment:
1. How are the push buttons connected in Figure 3?
2. How many paths are there for current flow in Figure 3?
3. In Figure 3, would the bell operate if one push button were pressed? Why?
4. If the circuit were broken at point A, would the bell operate if both push buttons were pressed? Explain.
5. If a wire were connected as in point B and the other push button pressed, would the bell ring? Why?
6. If the circuit failed to operate due to push button fault, how could each button be tested to determine the fault?
7. For what practical application could this type of circuit be used?

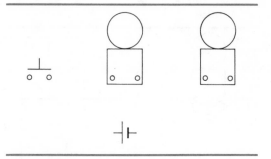

Figure 4 (a)

3. Wire the circuit of Figure 4.
4. Have the circuit checked by the instructor.
5. Test the circuit.

Assignment:
1. What is meant by a parallel circuit?
2. In the completed diagram of Figure 4 (a) place arrows showing the direction of current flow.
3. In Figure 4, if bell #1 burned out, would bell #2 operate? Why?

Introductory Electricity

4. If the circuit were broken at point A, which bell would operate? Explain.
5. If the circuit were broken at point B, which bell would operate? Why?
6. If a wire were connected across bell #2 as shown at C, which bell would operate? Explain.
7. How many paths are there for current flow in Figure 4?
8. What voltage does each bell take in Figure 4?
9. Draw a neat schematic diagram of four bells connected in parallel, controlled by one push button, using three dry cells in parallel.
10. In the circuit of Question 9, how much voltage does each bell take? Explain.
11. Name two applications for parallel bells.

Project #5

Objective: To wire one bell controlled by two push buttons connected in parallel
Materials: One bell, two push buttons, one dry cell, #18 T.W. bell wire
Procedure:
1. Make a neat drawing of Figure 5 (a) in your notes.
2. Study the completed diagram of Figure 5 and complete the diagram of Figure 5 (a). Connect the push buttons in parallel.
3. Wire the circuit of Figure 5.
4. Have the circuit checked by the instructor.
5. Test the circuit.

Assignment:
1. In the completed diagram of Figure 5 (a), place arrows showing the direction of current flow.
2. In Figure 5, if a jumper wire were connected across the push button as shown at A, what would happen?
3. How many paths are there for current flow in Figure 5?

4. If the circuit were broken at B in Figure 5 and the top push button were pressed, would the bell operate? Explain.
5. Draw a neat schematic diagram of one bell controlled by two push buttons in series with one dry cell.
6. Draw a neat schematic diagram of two bells, connected in parallel, controlled by two push buttons connected in parallel, with three dry cells in series.
7. In the circuit of Question 6, how much voltage does each bell take?
8. Name two applications for parallel push buttons.

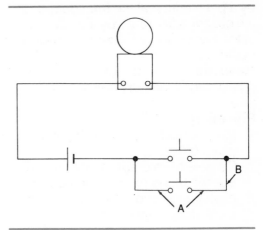

Figure 5

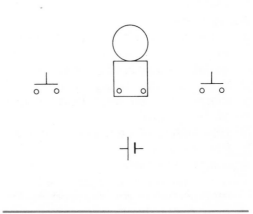

Figure 5 (a)

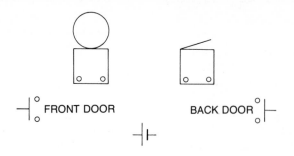

FRONT DOOR   BACK DOOR

Figure 6

Project #6

Objective: To wire a bell and buzzer connected so that the bell is operated by a push button at the front door and the buzzer is operated by a push button at the back door (front-and-back-door system)

Materials: One bell, one buzzer, two push buttons, one dry cell, #18 T.W. wire

Procedure:

1. Make a neat drawing of Figure 6 in your notes.
2. Complete the diagram of Figure 6 so that the bell is rung by the front-door push button and the buzzer by the back-door push button.
3. Wire the circuit of Figure 6.
4. Have the circuit checked by the instructor.
5. Test the circuit.

Assignment:

1. In the front-and-back-door system, why could two bells or two buzzers not be used instead of one of each?
2. In the completed diagram of Figure 6 place arrows showing the direction of current flow.
3. How many paths are there for current flow in Figure 6?
4. Suppose that when the front-door push button was pressed, the bell rang and when you released the push button, the bell kept ringing. What is the trouble?

5. What could be used for a source of supply instead of a dry cell?
6. If the bell burns out, will it affect the operation of the buzzer? Why?
7. If neither bell nor buzzer operate, where is the trouble likely to be?
8. Name two devices other than a bell and buzzer that may be used in this system.
9. Draw a neat schematic diagram of three bells, each controlled by its own push button with one dry cell.

Project #7

Objective: To wire a three-wire return call system

Materials: Two bells, two push buttons, 120 to 6 V bell transformer, #18 T.W. bell wire, source of 120 V ac

Procedure:

1. Make a neat drawing of Figure 7 in your notes.
2. Complete the diagram of Figure 7 so that push button 1 rings bell 1, and push button 2 rings bell 2. Only three wires are to run between the offices.
3. Wire the circuit of Figure 7.
4. Have the circuit checked by the instructor.
5. Test the circuit.

Assignment:

1. State the purpose of the three-wire return call system.

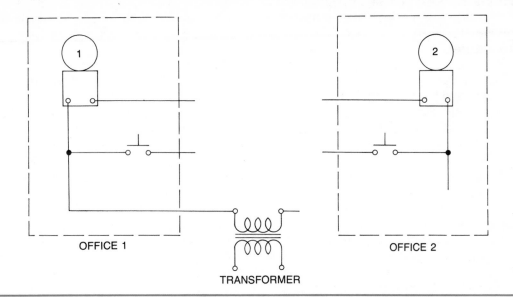

Figure 7

2. What is the purpose of the transformer?
3. Why is it used instead of a dry cell?
4. Name two places where this type of system can be used.
5. What is the advantage of the three-wire system over the four-wire system?
6. If both push buttons were pressed at the same time, would the bells ring? Why?

7. In the completed diagram of Figure 7, indicate by using arrows the direction of the current flow when both push buttons are pressed.

Project #8

Objective: To wire a front-and-back-door signal system using two-conductor annunciator wire

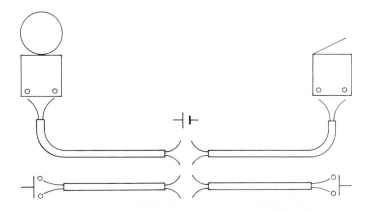

Figure 8

Materials: One bell, one buzzer, two push buttons, one dry cell, two-conductor annunciator wire

Procedure:

1. Make a neat drawing of Figure 8 in your notes.
2. Complete the diagram of Figure 8 so the bell is operated by the front-door push button and the buzzer is operated by the back-door push button.
3. Wire the completed circuit.
4. Have the circuit checked by the instructor.
5. Test the circuit.

Assignment:

1. Make a neat schematic diagram of Figure 8 and connect two lamps in the circuit. (One lamp is to light when the bell is operating and the other lamp is to light when the buzzer is operating.)
2. How are the lamps connected in the circuit?

Project #9

Objective: To wire a three-wire return call system using three-conductor annunciator wire

Materials: One bell, one buzzer, two push buttons, one dry cell, three-conductor annunciator wire

Procedure:

1. Make a neat diagram of Figure 9 in your notes.

2. Complete the diagram of Figure 9 so the bell will operate from push button 1 and the buzzer will operate from push button 2.
3. Wire the completed circuit.
4. Have the circuit checked by the instructor.
5. Test the circuit.

Assignment:

1. Make a neat schematic diagram of Figure 9 and connect two lamps in the circuit. (One lamp is to light when the bell is operating and the other lamp is to light when the buzzer is operating.)
2. How are the lamps connected in the circuit?

Project #10

Objective: To wire and test a two-coil chime system using two- and three-conductor annunciator wire

Materials: Two-coil chime, two push buttons, 120/10 V bell transformer, two- and three-conductor annunciator cable, source of 120 V ac power

Procedure: Part I

1. Wire the circuit as shown in Figure 10.
2. Have the circuit checked by the instructor.
3. Connect the transformer to a 120 V ac.

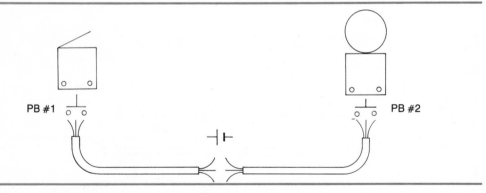

PB #1

PB #2

Figure 9

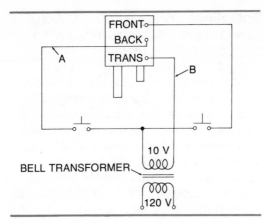

Figure 10

4. Test the circuit.

NOTE: In most modern homes, the wiring of chime circuits is a type of cable similar to bell telephone cable. The conductors are enclosed in a thermoplastic sheath (TW). All connections are usually made at one common point, usually at the transformer, which is located at the fuse panel. Figure 10 (a) shows the wiring of the cable brought to the transformer and ready for connections.

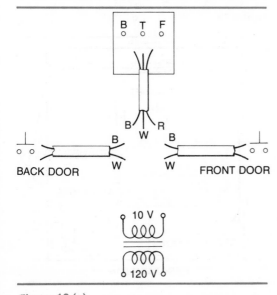

Figure 10 (a)

Procedure: Part II

1. Draw the circuit diagram of Figure 10 (a) in your notes.
2. Complete the circuit to operate as a front-and-back-door chime system.
3. Have the circuit checked by the instructor.
4. Wire the circuit and have it checked by the instructor.
5. Connect the source of power and test the circuit.

Assignment:

1. In Figure 10, if the circuit were broken at point A, would the chime operate? Explain.
2. In Figure 10, if the circuit were broken at point B, would the chime operate? Explain.
3. Explain how two tones are made by the chime.
4. What would happen if both push buttons were pressed at the same time? Explain.

Project #11

Objective: To wire and test a 4-point gravity drop manual annunciator system

Materials: Four-point gravity drop annunciator, four push buttons, 120/10 V bell transformer, annunciator wire, source of 120 V ac power

Procedure:

1. Make a drawing of Figure 11 in your notes.

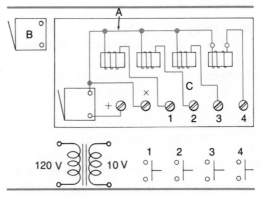

Figure 11

2. Complete the drawing of the circuit to operate the 4-point gravity drop annunciator.
3. Have the drawing of the circuit checked by the instructor.
4. Wire the circuit and have it checked by the instructor.
5. Connect to the source of power and test the circuit.

Assignment:
1. Why is it necessary to reset the annunciator?
2. If two push buttons were pressed at the same time, would they operate their respective drops? Why?
3. Can an annunciator be used without bells or buzzers? Explain.
4. If a wire were broken at push button 2, would it affect the operation of the drop coil? Explain.
5. How is the buzzer in the annunciator connected to the drop coils?
6. How is extension buzzer B connected to the circuit?
7. How are extension buzzers used with annunciators?
8. If the circuit were broken at point A, would the annunciator function? Explain.
9. If the circuit were broken at point C, would the annunciator function? Explain.

Project #12

Objective: To wire and test an open circuit burglar alarm system equipped with a constant ringing drop

Materials: Automatic ringer, one bell, one push button, annunciator wire, 6-10 V ac or dc power

NOTE: This circuit is widely used for burglar alarm systems in homes, shops, offices, warehouses, and out buildings on farms. The bell will ring continuously until the gravity drop is reset.

Operation: When the push button is closed, the current flows through the push button to the automatic ringer, through the coil of the ringer, and returns to the source to complete the circuit. The electromagnet is energized and attracts the armature. This releases the gravity drop, which makes contact with terminal 2 on the ringer and thus current flows through the bell. This completes the circuit and the bell will ring continuously until the gravity drop is reset. (Figures 12 and 12 (a))

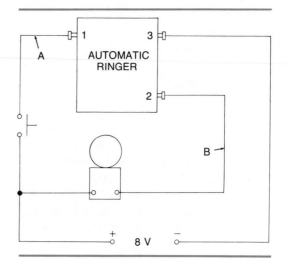

Figure 12

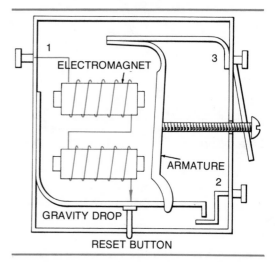

Figure 12 (a)

Introductory Electricity

Procedure:
1. Wire the circuit as shown in Figure 12.
2. Have the wiring checked by the instructor.
3. Connect to the source of power and test the circuit.

Assignment:
1. Would you use regular push buttons for a burglar alarm circuit? Why?
2. What type of circuit closers would you use for window contacts?
3. If you were wiring a house with this circuit, where would you suggest locating the bell and the automatic ringer? Why?
4. If the circuit were broken at point A in Figure 12, would the circuit operate? Explain.
5. If the circuit were broken at point B in Figure 12, would the circuit operate? Explain.
6. What is meant by open circuit?
7. Make a neat diagram showing all connections for an alarm circuit in a room with four windows.
8. Name three places that could utilize a burglar alarm system.

Index